Rivers Nursery
of Sawbridgeworth
THE ART OF PRACTICAL POMOLOGY

Early Rivers

Deep purple suddenly discovered
Hanging high, replacing
One bloom for another.
The plum baskets filled
In the afternoon innocence
Of past summers
And the clear sunlight
Of remembered shadows.
A tree loved for its earliness
And the repeating rituals
Of July.
Cream marbling the mauve juice
Of sweet fruit
And amber jam reflected
In rows of shining jars.
The heat hold of bottling
Felt in the bright scalding kitchen
Of hot days
Carrying the taste
Towards the cold time of autumn.

The tree has stood for sixty years.
Others have fallen
Crashed by hurricanes
Or the tortuous invasions of rot.
It comes into its own again
In winter
When other trees
Also stand leafless
Yet the dark inwardness of bark
Still holds its silhouette.

Juliet Bingley

Rivers' Early Fruit

Rivers Nursery
of Sawbridgworth
The Art of Practical Pomology

by Elizabeth Waugh

with articles by: Joseph Fitzgerald, Eugene Keddy, Paul Read,
John Sapsford, Tony Slingsby, Mike Thurlow, Denis Todhunter
and Eric Willison

Published by Rivers Nursery Site and Orchard Group
in association with Rockingham Press

First published in 2009

by Rivers Nursery Site and Orchard Group in association with Rockingham Press

www.riversnurseryorchard.org.uk; www.rockinghampress.com

ISBN 978-1-904851-32-5

Design by Perry Rule

Printed by Magazine Printing Company 0208 805 5000

Contents

List of Figures

Preface

This is the story of Thomas Rivers and Son Nursery (1725 -1987), its international and local prominence and the loss of traditional rural pursuits its demise represents.

It's a collection of voices. We were fortunate to have funding for an oral history project from Awards for All during the course of which we were able to get on record the individual memories of a number of those who had been connected with the nursery and generously gave their time to talk to adult and student interviewers. We also had contact with others who were happy to tell stories even if they wouldn't be recorded. The search for primary sources yielded other voices. The voice of the greatest Thomas Rivers, of the nineteenth century (1798 - 1877), the practical pomologist, is heard well through his prolific writing which has a workmanlike colloquial manner. One of the understandings I came to in the course of this work is that those who write and are written about are more likely to survive as individual identities, hardly a revelation if I had been listening properly to Shakespeare and the Elizabethans who told us that long ago.

I have also asked various people with specific information to write it up in their own words. These interesting articles have been set with the relevant chapters, adding depth to the perception of how things were in the past or are now. The final article gives an exacting scientific view of ancestry of the trees on the present day orchard site and their value in the canon of Thomas Rivers cultivars.

These voices and how they connect to or contradict one another reminds us that history is no more than a collection of memories and descriptions which might not even come close to a dispassionate 'factual' account. We are our memories and who we are influences how we remember. For me this testimony comes close to touching the texture and sense of everyday life and shows how accumulating layers produces some overall meaning.

The new material was added to the Rivers Archive that we had been collecting for some years. The book draws together everything we could find from all sources available. The archive used to be largely a collection of paper, some original such as Rivers catalogues given to us, or reproduced from the County Archives, Lindley Library and elsewhere. Now with the oral histories it has a more authentic feel.

It's a local social and economic history, though by no means comprehensive, featuring a horticulture business. However, this local scene reflects what was happening nationally. There are sections on how the company was likely to have been set up and organised and, using some of the testimony we have gathered during the oral history project, information on horticultural practices during different periods and sections on people and their positions in the company and what contributions they made. Then there are chapters on the decline of the company followed by the rescue of a remainder of the site and its development as a community orchard. The central section concerns the third Thomas and his vision upon which the long-lasting reputation of the company rests and without which it might have been just another well-run, timely provincial nursery business.

I hope that this account comes a way toward capturing the outline of an outstanding enterprise which, through lack of records, is in danger of being forgotten or in its final incarnation as a community orchard, being destroyed.

**Elizabeth Waugh,
October 2009**

Acknowledgements

Most of all, this book has been made possible by the generous involvement of many local residents, who have shared their memories and their photographs, made time to give interviews during the Oral History project, written up their thoughts and have been interested in being part of this work. Through their help Rivers Archive has been expanded - we hope it will continue to grow through further interviews and donations of materials.

I would like to thank one person in particular, John Sapsford, who drawing on his own lucid personal history records has been very helpful to the groups restoring the orchard over the years. He has been of particular support to me in the preparation of this text, proof-reading it all for inaccuracies and helping me to get as close to the past as I can.

I have asked some with extensive relevant or expert knowledge to contribute articles - none said no, taking time from busy lives to write up some aspect of information that develops our understanding of horticulture as practised by Rivers Nursery. I am very grateful for their participation.

The staff at Hertfordshire Archives and Local Studies have been most helpful through a succession of visits as have those in other libraries consulted over the years. Now that preliminary enquiries can be carried out by email and collections searched on-line the process of finding materials has been made more efficient, though the work of digesting the implications of information continues to be as challenging and as interesting as ever.

The Rivers Nursery Site and Orchard Group - those individuals most involved with the Rivers heritage on a day-to-day basis - have been consulted as the book developed and have given back-up assistance as needed. This book is part of a joint local effort to consider the contribution of the Nursery and conserve its legacy.

Last and very important I appreciate my family - who seem to develop new skills constantly in response to my requests - and my friends, among them the designer Perry Rule, who all have given me unwavering regard and continuous support.

Elizabeth Waugh

Published with the Support of Awards for All

Supported by
The National Lottery®
through Awards for All

AWARDS FOR ALL

Chapter One
The Land

View from above - Rivers land and situation

Looked at from above, the land somewhat to the west and south of Sawbridgeworth village in East Hertfordshire is seen to be open fields, a level plateau extending to the west and tipping sharply east to the main road and then beyond down to the River Stort. Even now, almost three hundred years after the first Rivers established a business in this situation, this view encompasses the same fundamental elements it had then. Though the housing has expanded and incursions have been made into fields immediately adjacent to the built areas, the Green Belt legislation has preserved wide expanses of open rural countryside bordering the river valley. The qualities of this land have been the key to the continuing development of a population centre here based on agricultural pursuits.

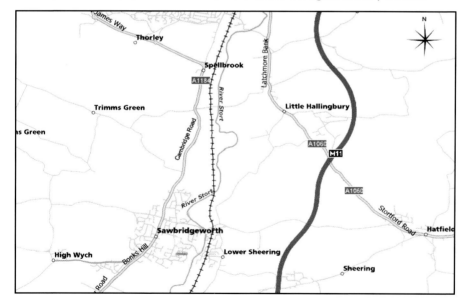

A schematic map of the locality of contemporary Sawbridgeworth showing:
the River Stort that forms the boundary between Hertfordshire and Essex; the roads and railway that link Cambridge and the north with London and the south; the High Wych road bordering most of the Rivers Nursery land; the pattern of clustered town and village housing with stretches of agricultural land between.

Figure 1.1

The Stort, winding gently from north east to south west, forms a natural boundary between Hertfordshire and Essex - though the landscape and soil quality is continuous on both sides - and is the only natural boundary for the county of Hertfordshire, others having been devised and altered by administrative means at different periods. As the Stort continues south it meets the River Lea and flows on toward London. Beginning on the canalised Stort, modern narrow boats are able to take a slow voyage from Sawbridgeworth even as far as Regents Park in central London. Beside the Stort is the railway line, completed as a through line in 1845, also making its way from points north to London. The main road, the A1184, edging the Rivers land, leads to the M11 and on to the metropolis. From this vantage point above the Rivers land, beyond Harlow New Town to the south, might be seen the tall edifices of Canary Wharf just visible in the misty atmosphere, twenty-five miles or so away.

This area, now Green Belt with farmland intersected by narrow roads, has been identified by contemporary governments as a prime development location for new housing near the capital and a quickly expanding airport. However, for the moment it is still characterised by the features that allowed a horticultural firm positioned here to grow and prosper over nearly three centuries. The soil quality and the climate offered the potential for planting; the village population offered the workforce; roads, rail and the river the transport; London and the local prosperity deriving in part from proximity to the city as well as to grand and small local landowners, the markets.

Now as in the past Sawbridgeworth is a pleasant place. The aesthetic qualities of the landscape deriving from the temperate beauty of eastern Hertfordshire seen here in the Stort Valley are embodied in the gentle rise and fall of the land forms, the quietly flowing rivers, the green crop land and the easily grown plantings of hedges, copses, parkland, avenues of trees and the like. Once off the major roads, there is a sense of enduring rural peace and continuity with the past. There is something of a 'secret landscape of narrow winding lanes and isolated farmhouses' that remains.[1] The landscape here remains a formation deriving from an ancient agrarian past - expansive vistas over fields threaded by farm tracks with borders of close-clustered housing. Local livelihoods until recently depended on farming or agricultural specialisms such as the two most important local trades of the nineteenth century, malting and horticulture, or on the associated employment supporting agricultural production. The slow rhythms of the countryside dominated the pace of life.

Ancient times, settlement and farming

The soil and climate have supported farming over millennia. Sawbridgeworth is located in the boulder clay plateau of eastern Hertfordshire. The earth is formed from clay mixed with chalky chunks scraped off the more northern land by glaciers drifting south, and deposited over the underlying chalk bedrock as the climate warmed after the ending of the last Ice Age. Small brooks and streams flow east from this land into the Stort river and eventually the Lea. The soil is fertile, well drained and relatively malleable even for stone age implements, enabling agricultural activity through the ages. This is the most rural area in Hertfordshire. Stone tools that have been found in the Stort valley over many thousands of years testify to the passing presence of nomadic tribes and to early settlements. The Bishop's Stortford Museum holds a small collection of such stone implements.

Late Mesolithic
flint hand axe,
Sawbridgeworth,
c 5000 BC.
Reproduced by kind permission
of Bishop's Stortford Museum
Figure 1.2

Neolithic hand axe,
Sawbridgeworth,
c 3000-2000 BC
Reproduced by kind permission
of Bishop's Stortford Museum
Figure 1.3

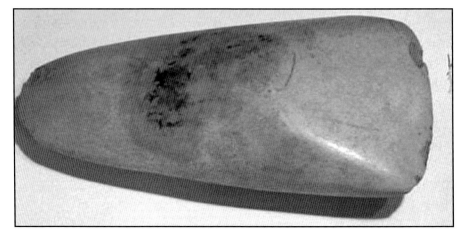

The climate too has proved to be right for growing crops. Despite fluctuations in temperature over time such as recorded during the Little Ice Age of the sixteenth and seventeenth centuries - during which there were periods of protracted snowfall and lengthy freezes - the climate of this region is temperate, not very hot in summer nor very cold in winter, suited to growing grains such as barley, enabling later the vigorous local malting industry, and other crops such as saffron in early times. For a horticultural enterprise many desirable plants would grow well, though some of the tender cropping fruit varieties such as the fashionable grapes, oranges, peaches and nectarines of the nineteenth century required protection in glasshouses.

Farming has been continuous in the Sawbridgeworth area for at least six thousand years, from a period when hunter gatherers first began to work the land for their living, and to settle and establish communities. Evidence of early Neolithic people has been discovered here above the marshland bordering the Stort, just east of Pishiobury Park. 'The combination of fertile soils, good access to water, good communications and the presence of raw materials, such as flint for tools, made Sawbridgeworth a favoured area for Neolithic activity and it contains some of the best Neolithic evidence in the region.'[2] The only example in the county of Hertfordshire of an earthwork of the kind known as a causewayed enclosure was discovered here. The traces of ditches and a raised earth platform were spotted as crop marks during aerial survey.

This causeway is situated on flat ground, on the first rise above the river beyond the boggy flood plain. This field adjacent to the riverbed is likely to have been less heavily forested and one more easily cleared early of its woody cover. From this point the view takes in not only the drop down to the river but on beyond the marsh and wet meadows across the river to the rising ground on the east side of the valley. It is thought to have formed a meeting point between different social groups divided by the river and its alluvial basin. The significance of this meeting point within the developing society of the period is not clear. It seems to have a limited practical function but perhaps as Tom Williamson suggests, 'we have hints here of another landscape, one of myth and ritual, of sacred rivers and associated enclosures'. [3]

From prehistoric times into the Saxon period, there is evidence that agricultural activity on this fertile land supported a larger population here than in other areas in Hertfordshire and above average for England. The first settlements began in the river valleys and moved out, clearing woodland of its native cover of hazel, briar, hawthorn, blackthorn, oak and the like. Even now on land left to its own devices for a few years, a scrub of similar native brush will quickly take over. Continuing cultivation and an increasing population of people accompanied by a greater number of grazing animals maintained the cleared land, creating grassland which on this soil and in this climate develops naturally. People clustered in settlements with fields stretching out beyond. In this way Neolithic people began to change the landscape from ancient woodland to the agrarian landscape still in evidence today.

Roman period

The Roman period from the first conquest by Julius Caesar in 43AD through the departure of the Romans early in the fifth century brought increased

organised farming to the east Hertfordshire area. There is evidence of
Roman settlement on both sides of the Stort valley where isolated
farmsteads were established on the fertile land and in more clustered
housing such as in Bishop's Stortford where coins, pottery and implements,
including farm tools, have been found in various areas. In Harlow there is
the foundation of an important temple with associated finds of bronze, glass
and pottery. Evidence of a Romano-British burial area was revealed by the
discovery of a number of skeletons in Sawbridgeworth. The area continued
to be utilised for production of crops and the settled way of life associated
with the Romans and the native population they controlled. The properties
of the land were exploited by the Romans as the means to a prosperous life
as continued to be the case as later populations followed on. Many of the
farmsteads continued in places of earlier settlements and after the Romans
left others continued to develop favoured land sites around the Stort valley. [4]

Saxon period

East Saxon territory, incorporated in the county name Essex, and taking in
the eastern areas of Hertfordshire, was located, without any strict
boundaries, in the valleys of the eastern rivers including the Stort. Similar to
the likely meeting point represented by the prehistoric causeway, crossing
points of whatever form - perhaps fords - have remained important. Perhaps
the Sawbridgeworth settlement in the Stort Valley grew in Saxon times
because of a significant crossing point over the Stort. Even now, the Hyde
Hall estate rests on a curving piece of land that projects, if the county map
is consulted, over the River Stort, past the river delineation line and remains
part of Hertfordshire, despite its position in what is over the river in Essex.

This vagary in the county boundary probably protects a river crossing positioned there from very early times, as well as the Manor that later was positioned there. East Hertfordshire has remained a boundary area, sharing modern administrative ties - health districts for example - between Essex across the river Stort and Hertfordshire.

That the Saxons settling in the region following the withdrawal of Roman forces in the fifth century AD must have continued the development of farming practices and clearing of timber for crop-growing land is not known from archaeological finds. Little has survived here from this period. Houses constructed of natural materials such as timber and straw rather than the more durable brick and tile of the villas of the Romans can be predicated as having been built here, based on finds of the period elsewhere. It is likely that Saxons settled in areas near to Roman settlements, where the same features of cleared, well-watered, fertile lands made for good farming, but not in the same sites or same buildings.

More durable than houses have been the names given to farmsteads in the Saxon period, which survive into the twenty-first century as key points on the maps of the area. Sawbridgeworth, spelled on maps even as late as the Dury and Andrews of 1766 as 'Sabridgeworth' may refer to the East Saxon king Saebert compounded with -worth indicating an enclosed area - so probably may mean Saebert's farm. High Wych was a wic, a specialised farm, in this case a dairy farm. Redrick was a cattle farm. These early names indicate both how early the land was cleared for farming purposes and the viability of the land which has continued since then under cultivation. The latter two farms are in the immediate vicinity of what later became the expanding acreage of the Rivers business, and both or some portion of each were eventually purchased by the Rivers family. Hertfordshire county as an administrative area, laid out to respect the boundaries of the important estates of the time, was established around the tenth century and is noted in the Anglo-Saxon Chronicle as a place-name in this saga of the history of the Anglo-Saxon people

Medieval period

It is notable that in 1086, at the date of the great accounting of the Domesday Book, cleared, arable land covered an area almost as large as was recorded in the 1838 Tithe Award, amounting to about two/thirds of the Parish. Due to the availability of good farming land, Sawbridgeworth was at this time counted as the most valuable estate in the county.

As part of the complicated systems of duties and rights that existed during the medieval period of great estates in Sawbridgeworth parish, there were common fields where peasant farmers held strips to cultivate, in order to make their own livings over and above what was owed in kind, labour and other service to the lords who owned the land. These strips could be passed on to their heirs on payment of a fee to the lord. Gradually villeins came to be able to sell on their own land. The most important crop was grain, some of which came to be sold for increasing profit in London.

From the fifteenth century

By the fifteenth and sixteenth centuries society had undergone a change as was evident from the ownership of land. No longer was the land altogether in the hands of powerful lords, concentrated in huge manors. Smaller holdings were being developed by yeoman farmers building land holdings from earlier consolidation of small parcels of land. Merchants whose wealth had been made in London had started buying property in Hertfordshire. Local farmers and tradesmen were prospering and building homes and business premises, many of which still stand today forming the central section of Sawbridgeworth village.

Farms and farming continued to be as important in the local economy as ever. Parsonage Farm on the north-west side of Sawbridgeworth village, surveyed in the mid-seventeenth century, was leased from the Dean and Chapter of Westminster and rental was paid, some in money and in goods. An example of what made up a prosperous farm of the time, Parsonage Farm included a gate house, brewhouse, malt-house, bakehouse, cart house, hog house, wood house, two kitchens and a lodging chamber for servants. On the property were three fishponds, a number of large orchards and two smaller ones, a twelve acre croft of timber and arable and pasture land. When farms changed hands, the farm-buildings and other features went with the land. When the Rivers family began to acquire land, buildings were included and could not only be used as family homes but be rented out to others or used as tied cottages for labourers working for the business.[5]

In terms of services and transport, the Stort River until the end of the sixteenth century, before canalisation, was navigable if meandering - as we can see by the course of what remains of the un-canalised river today - and must have been used to market local goods and crops. A good road into London came in the early seventeenth century when the early Stuart kings travelled to Newmarket frequently, following the construction of Newmarket Palace by King James I between 1606 and 1610.

Undulating agricultural landscape of the Stort valley
Photograph Adam Waugh
Figure 1.4

From the earliest settled times the draw of east Hertfordshire has been its good farming land. This has served saffron growers as well as maltsters. The land coupled with good transport links made it possible for the produce to be taken to the ever-growing metropolitan area to the south as well as to be distributed locally. A horticulture business could make use of these same attributes of the area. These kinds of industry in turn preserved the landscape and the agrarian character of the place and fostered a certain way of life that flowered in the nineteenth century Rivers business. It might be said that it largely continued its rural idyll until present times.

When John Rivers came to Sawbridgeworth about 1725 and acquired Bonks Hill house, then a simple farmhouse built in the previous century, with a relatively small area of perhaps twenty acres immediately beside it for cultivation, he had found an ideal situation for horticulture. The physical qualities of the nursery site were well described in an article in a horticultural journal of the nineteenth century.

> Placed upon a considerable elevation, and bounded on one side by the road from Sawbridgeworth, and a well-wooded park beyond, the nursery is well sheltered from the south-east. The other boundaries seem to melt into arable or pasture land…the whole surface is diversified with here a gentle slope, there a fine valley and again a stretch of level ground. The cultural and climatic advantages of such a surface will be at once obvious to practical pomologists….The soil itself is well-nigh as varied as the surface. Large portions of it consist of light loam resting on sand; others alluvial loam, with a substratum of brick-earth; and a stronger loam, resting on a solid calcareous clayey bottom. …Hence almost everything can be well grown here. [6]

Notes

1. Lionel Munby, *The Hertfordshire Landscape,* in *The Making of the English Landscape Series,* (London, 1977), p. 189.
2. V. Seddon and S. Bryant, *Sawbridgeworth: Extensive Urban Survey Project Assessment Report,* part of archaeological surveys by English Heritage, 1999 in Hertfordshire Archives and Local Studies.
3. T. Williamson, *The Origins of Hertfordshire* (Manchester, 2000), p. 33.
4. Sawbridgeworth W.E.A., *The Story of Sawbridgeworth, Book 1 From Prehistory to the Present,* edited by Lionel Munby, (1966), pp. 5 - 10.
5. *Ibid.,* p. 53.
6. D.T. Fish, 'Garden Memoranda: Rivers' Nurseries, Sawbridgeworth' in *The Gardeners' Chronicle and Agricultural Gazette, 1866,* p. 1119.

Chapter Two
The Eighteenth Century: the Establishment of a Horticulture Business

John Rivers comes to Sawbridgeworth

According to the family tree in the leaflet *250 Years of Thomas Rivers and Son Ltd. of Sawbridgeworth,* the first of the Rivers family, John, arrived in Sawbridgeworth in 1725 from Basildon in Berkshire. Little can be discovered about him, his previous work or his activity that resulted in establishing the family horticulture business. However, looking at the Sawbridgeworth of that period and using later archival references to the Rivers family provides the scope for some deductions about how the firm might have begun.

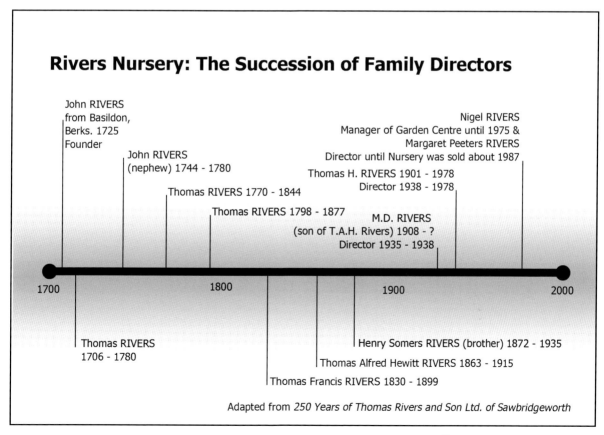

Rivers Nursery: The Succession of Family Directors

John RIVERS
from Basildon,
Berks. 1725
Founder

John RIVERS
(nephew) 1744 - 1780

Thomas RIVERS 1770 - 1844

Thomas RIVERS 1798 - 1877

Nigel RIVERS
Manager of Garden Centre until 1975 &
Margaret Peeters RIVERS
Director until Nursery was sold about 1987

Thomas H. RIVERS 1901 - 1978
Director 1938 - 1978

M.D. RIVERS
(son of T.A.H. Rivers) 1908 - ?
Director 1935 - 1938

1700   1800   1900   2000

Thomas RIVERS
1706 - 1780

Henry Somers RIVERS (brother) 1872 - 1935

Thomas Alfred Hewitt RIVERS 1863 - 1915

Thomas Francis RIVERS 1830 - 1899

Adapted from *250 Years of Thomas Rivers and Son Ltd. of Sawbridgeworth*

Eighteenth century Sawbridgeworth had already much of the characteristic structure that features in the lives of residents today. In the centre of the village many of the houses both great and small in what is now perceived as the historic central section had been built. There were many homes owned by the rising middle classes and gentry as well as housing for increasingly prosperous tradesmen and craftsmen. According to the trade directories of the early nineteenth century, there were carpenters, tailors, grocers, horse dealers, bakers and the like as well as labourers living in the centre of the town. Farmers profited from growing barley to make malt for beer - a trade that expanded enormously in the East Hertfordshire. The Dury and Andrews map shows a cluster of village housing in Sawbridgeworth and singles out as well the great estates of the area.

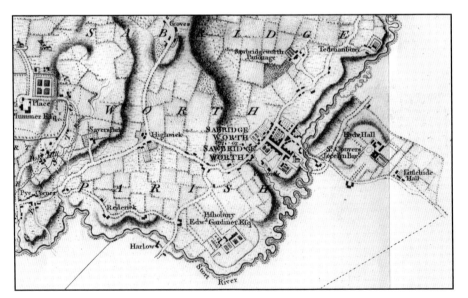

Detail of the county map by Dury and Andrews, 1766, showing the Sawbridgeworth area, bordering the meandering course of the Stort River.

Reproduced by kind permission of the Hertfordshire Archives and Local Studies

Figure 2.1

Most of the economy of the time continued as in previous eras to be derived from the productivity of the land. The Land Tax returns of 1712, 1781 and 1831 show that 'a large proportion of taxable wealth [on land and buildings] belonged to a few and this proportion increased steadily over the century'.[2] That is, a few great estates possessed most of the land. However, rental property was cheap. This may have allowed someone such as the first John Rivers in 1725 to make a start on a profitable horticultural business on land that was for the most part rented rather than owned.

Even the vicar had his living indirectly from the land. The first record of the parish church, Great St. Mary, is in the Domesday Book, when the living is mentioned: the priest of the Church is rated at one hide, a measure based on land productivity. By the eighteenth century, the vicars were supported by the tithe system which was also a tax on land and property. This system, based as we know on the payment of one/tenth of produce or income as a tax, continued despite the complications arising from many factors including the transfer over the centuries of many tithe rights from the Church to secular landowners, and then to the Crown. Further complications arose from the change in what was grown. For example saffron was a profitable crop in Sawbridgeworth parish before the sixteenth century and vicars derived a good living from the tithe owed them on saffron. When corn became the main crop, the tithe on corn did not go to the vicar whose living was badly affected. The tithe system ended in 1836 when tithes were replaced by a rent charge decided by a Tithe Commission. The tithe maps of 1838 which record land ownership show what land was owned or leased by the Rivers family and are an important tool in tracing the position and extent of their holdings.

Crops raised on the fertile and productive agricultural land found markets not only in the immediate local area but in the nearby metropolitan area of London. Great landowners profited but so did the craftsmen, tradesmen and gentry of the town. House building and refurbishment - for example putting brick facades on earlier structures - enhanced the town centre. Sawbridgeworth was a prosperous town in a prosperous area, although its economic dominance in East Hertfordshire as recorded in the Domesday Book, had over the centuries been overtaken by the growth of Bishop's Stortford nearby. An indication of the differing status of these two towns was that the right to hold a market in Sawbridgeworth was given in 1222 and markets continued on different days, granted to different important families, until the eighteenth century. Then Sawbridgeworth markets ceased, maybe because the one at Bishop's Stortford was more important. After the canalisation of the Stort in 1769 malting businesses flourished in Bishop's Stortford, although the importance of Ware as a maltings town was never overtaken. Sawbridgeworth too had a malting industry but never as large as in Stortford and with one of its important local maltings a branch of a Stortford company.

Better transport

Improvements in transport links were very important in allowing businesses to thrive. During the eighteenth century important improvements came both to the road system and the river. There had been a well-established road system over the ages, as reflected in the importance of estates bordering the river and holding a crossing point, as in the example of Hyde Hall, at the position of the road crossing the town from Essex to the east over what was called High Bridge and continuing west into the town. There was also an important road north to Bishop's Stortford.

However, the road south to London caused problems as in the early part of the century it was neither straight nor direct. The road west to High Wych, spelled High Wick on maps of this period, coming into the road at Bonks Hill (perhaps named after Robert de Baunck, a land owner of 1278) just south of the village centre, was used as the main road going west until it diverted south again. This bend in the road and the steepness of the hill caused transport problems. It seems that this road was better from 1763 because it had come into the hands of a Turnpike Trust - composed naturally of the town's leading citizens - in 1744 which enabled trustees to charge a toll to road users. The revenue allowed improvements to be carried out. However, the road continued to cause problems as testified by complaints from the controller of the mails which had begun to use the London road through Sawbridgeworth in 1787.

These problems were solved eventually by proposals from 1818 on; work was eventually carried out in 1831 for widening the road around the entrance to the Pishiobury estate and for a new bridge over the Stort further south towards Harlow. These discussions involving landholders on each side of the London road are of particular interest. The landholder to the east was the owner of Pishiobury, Mrs. Milles, at the time the greatest landholder in the area, paying 39% of the total tax as seen from the Land Tax return of 1831, and the landholder to the west was Mr. Rivers. It is to be seen from the various records that the Rivers business and the property pertaining to it was firmly established and growing by the mid to late eighteenth century. As a man of business and property, Mr. Rivers was becoming prominent in local affairs and was expected to have a voice in community decision making. He had an important part in enabling transport by road to London to be made easier.

Transport via the Stort River also improved with the opening of the canal in 1769. The engineering works were carried out by George Jackson, who later became Sir George Duckett, and other Stortford businessmen so that the Stort once again became navigable. Its meandering route had become gradually choked by weeds and silt over time. There were two locks in Sawbridgeworth, one at either end of the village, and a wharf, all easily accessible by road for wagons transporting goods of various kinds and especially useful later for the maltings located by the river. The wharf was located on the ancient and still major road to Hyde Hall and Chelmsford. This became Station Rd after the railway was completed as a through line from London to Norwich in 1845. That this brought more trade and employment to the area is shown by the fact that traffic on the canalised river doubled in the last twenty years of the century.

The restored Keeper's Cottage at Sheering Mill Lock on the River Stort with the G. D. emblem for George Jackson over the door
Reproduced by kind permission of Mr. and Mrs. Goodwin

Figure 2.2

It is unlikely that the Rivers company used the canal much as a means of delivering plants or fruit to buyers as it was too slow a method of transport. The railway, shown on the Rivers catalogues as the delivery point, was favoured and the speed with which letters were delivered is notable. As described in a later chapter, between Charles Darwin and Rivers a correspondence flew as it were by train with only a matter of a couple of days between one sending a letter and the other replying.

Despite increasing trade, there was during the late eighteenth century a great deal of poverty too. The Poor Law records show an increase in what was spent from local rates to maintain the poor of the parish. As the great estate owners were increasing the extent of their ownership of land and the tradesmen were becoming more prosperous, the social conditions for the poor were becoming worse. Charitable individuals also made contributions towards the welfare of the poor, supplementing what was given from the rates.[3]

In the eighteenth century farming was still the main occupation for most people, whether involved in the labour or drawing their income from the produce. As a prosperous area with increasingly good transportation links, Sawbridgeworth was surely a good location in which to set up a horticulture business. Closely linked with farming both in methods and skills required from labourers, the business would have been able to draw on a suitable workforce and make use of the fertile land of the area.

The nursery trade in the eighteenth century

Whether John Rivers came to Sawbridgeworth in 1725 as a experienced nurseryman, or with plans to establish a nursery business, or perhaps as a farmer is not known. However, by 1838, the considerable Rivers land marked on the Tithe Map is identified in the section called 'description of land' for the most part as 'nursery' and in the section 'state of cultivation' mostly as 'garden', with other areas named as 'arable' and one section as 'market garden'. [4] Pigot's Directory of 1839 lists Thomas Rivers and Son, London road under Nursery and Seedsmen, one of two such businesses in Sawbridgeworth, the other of which must have been much smaller and long since disappeared. [5]

In the County Archives in Hertford, there is a collection of papers from the Rivers Nursery deposited in 1981 by Tony Slingsby, a manager at the period when the last Thomas Rivers had died and the business was breaking up, and not long before the remaining land was sold. This deposit contains interesting documents from the nineteenth and twentieth centuries, but none earlier than 1840.

But what of the early days of the business? In the County Archives is a sales agreement of 1789, a separate document not part of any bundle of papers which records a transaction between Samuel Mason, gentleman of Walkernbury, near Stevenage in central Hertfordshire, and John Rivers of 'Sabridgeworth', gardener. This John Rivers is likely to be the 'John Rivers, nephew of the second John Rivers, retired 1782' recorded on the family tree. John Rivers is paying altogether £900 for 'All that Messuage or Farm House with the Lands Grounds and other Appurtenances thereonto belonging situate at a place called Highwich in the Parish of Sabridgeworth in the said County of Hertford being part Freehold and part Copyhold.'

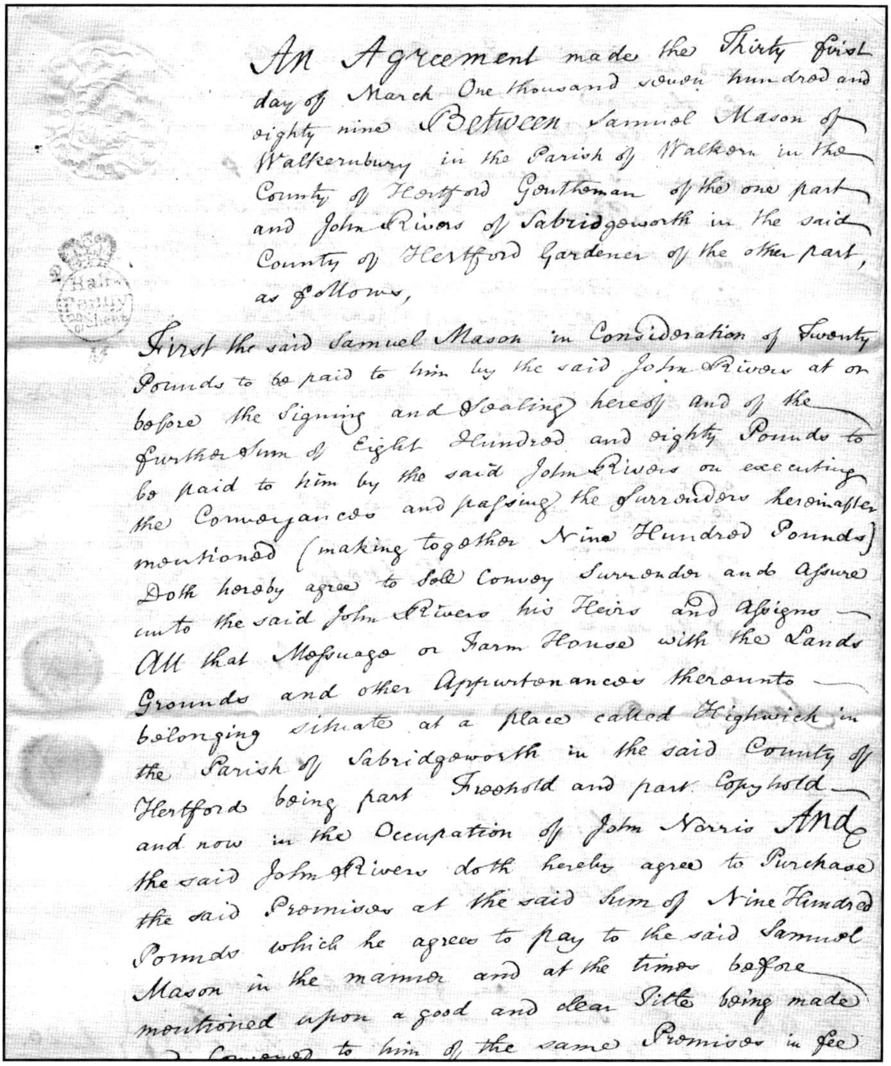

An Agreement made the Thirty first day of March One thousand seven hundred and eighty nine Between Samuel Mason of Walkernbury in the Parish of Walkern in the County of Hertford Gentleman of the one part and John Rivers of Sabridgeworth in the said County of Hertford Gardener of the other part, as follows,

First the said Samuel Mason in Consideration of Twenty Pounds to be paid to him by the said John Rivers at or before the Signing and Sealing hereof and of the further Sum of Eight Hundred and eighty Pounds to be paid to him by the said John Rivers on executing the Conveyances and passing the Surrenders hereinafter mentioned (making together Nine Hundred Pounds) Doth hereby agree to Sell Convey Surrender and Assure unto the said John Rivers his Heirs and Assigns — All that Messuage or Farm House with the Lands Grounds and other Appurtenances thereunto belonging situate at a place called Highwich in the Parish of Sabridgeworth in the said County of Hertford being part Freehold and part Copyhold and now in the Occupation of John Norris And the said John Rivers doth hereby agree to Purchase the said Premises at the said Sum of Nine Hundred Pounds which he agrees to pay to the said Samuel Mason in the manner and at the times before mentioned upon a good and clear Title being made and Conveyed to him of the same Premises in fee

A section of the Sales Agreement between John Rivers and Samuel Mason, 1789.

Reproduced by kind permission of Hertfordshire Archives and Local Studies (Document 28111)

Figure 2.3

This is very likely not his first purchase of land, but it is the only one of which a record exists in the County Archive. There is on this agreement no record of the amount of land purchased in this transaction, nor an accompanying map. The sum is considerable so the company must have thrived in its gardening business in the years since the first John Rivers came to Sawbridgeworth. Family tradition suggests that the first land purchase was of what became Bonk's Hill House, not as grand as it later became. From this likely first location on the London road, the business spread, acquiring land little by little perhaps in long tracts as seen on the Tithe Map of 1838 as laid out by medieval field systems. It is this map that first gives us a view of the extent of the Rivers land ownership. Records of Rivers ownership here shows somewhat scattered holdings in the area west of Sawbridgeworth village and in the village itself of considerable acreage. If the original land holding that was purchased with Bonks Hill House was small, of about twenty acres or so, spreading west from behind the house, there was considerable land still marked on early nineteenth century maps as common land - Mansfield Common, Broadfield Common - immediately adjacent, and this land was eventually taken over by the Nursery as it spread towards High Wych.[6]

The growth and development of the Rivers Nursery follows to a great extent the general development of the nursery trade in England. From the Norman period there is evidence of a cult of gardening and of trade in seed grains surplus from great estates and monastic gardens. After the dissolution of the monasteries and the loss of specialised gardening by monks and friars, there came to exist commercial nurseries by about the sixteenth century to meet the need for raising the best varieties of plants or producing viable seed stock. During the age of discovery and exploration of the sixteenth and seventeenth centuries and later, the nursery trade took advantage of the interest in new species with introductions from British colonies in North America and temperate places. Later towards 1800 there was an opportunity to meet the interest in sub-tropical and tropical species which had a need for glass. Wealthy landowners, after 1845 and the abolition of the tax on glass, were able to afford to build glasshouses to protect tender plants. Enhanced status was brought to owners of country houses by the unique qualities of the produce of their kitchen gardens and orchards and later their conservatories and glasshouses, as it appeared on their dinner tables. Its excellence, that is its beauty, flavour, abundance or early appearance, all were a source of pride and effort on the part of gardeners. This interest in food crops is accompanied as well by the interest in the aesthetic effect of gardening in the landscape surrounding great houses and in the gardens of the genteel where orchards as well as ornamental plants were used as embellishments, good for walking in as well as for provision of the table.[7]

Gardening in the eighteenth century continued as previously to have a vital importance in providing food for the family table, no matter what social rank that family might have. It is clear from looking at the survey (probably from the eighteenth century in the Westminster Abbey land records) of Parsonage Farm in Sawbridgeworth that orchards and kitchen fields amounting to twenty-three acres were an important part of the land holding.[8] It was these areas that were to grow the food for the more important families of the farm as well as for the labouring families.

In the town itself as well as on farms, most village homes had at least a few fruit trees on their plots demonstrated by the survival in the modern gardens of the older houses of a few gnarled fruit trees that were planted at some time in the past and are part of a continuing habit of cultivation. There is no doubt that in the eighteenth century all who had large or small plots of ground grew their own vegetables as well, necessary in the absence of shops to feed the family. There are large areas, 'The Orchards' in Sawbridgeworth for example, where houses have now replaced lost orchards belonging to the larger houses.

That there was a growing interest in gardening after 1660 and beyond might be partly due to the royalist exiles returning from the continent where there was continuing interest in gardens and plants growing in warmer climates. Books on gardening appeared in the eighteenth century, such as that by John Lawrence of 1717 who writes of 'Gardening being of late Years become the general Delight and Entertainment of the Nobility and Gentry, as well as the Clergy of this Nation'. [9] Because of this interest and the demand it stimulated, wider based than in previous times, the nursery trade grew too. John Harvey in his book on early nurserymen calculates that there were about fifteen nurseries in greater London by 1700 and about thirty around London and Colchester by 1730.[10]

In this case, if John Rivers came to Sawbridgeworth to place himself to meet the demand for high quality plants, he caught the tide of interest in horticulture. He was able to establish a business that was in a good location for supplying the adjacent areas and the metropolitan area beyond, due to position, transport facilities and good growing land.

However, the details of how the Rivers business was founded and funded are not available. Even in the eighteenth century, the

> ...need to carry large stocks, and spend money on greenhouses and skilled workers, made nurseries expensive to run; in the 1740s it was estimated between

£500 and £1000 capital was needed to start a business...The structure of the trade was relatively simple. Nurseries sold stocks of plants and trees produced by themselves, new plants imported from abroad or bought from other nurseries, and seed purchased from seedsmen. They sold direct to the public, either in person or by mail order. [11]

Bonks Hill House and garden in the eighteenth century gave directly onto the London road as is known from the Turnpike discussions. From there the nursery was in a good place to conduct a plant trade. As is clear from maps, Rivers land holdings gradually spread out mostly from the rear of the property over farmland and former common land towards High Wych village to the west, giving more and more space for growing areas and later glasshouses, with access to road at the front of the property.

That the Rivers business established itself firmly and thrived during the eighteenth century, placing itself in a position to become an important nationally recognised company in the century that followed, is a testament not only to the business acumen, talent and energy of the family members involved. It is also due to the firm's location in East Hertfordshire. Here were found the good horticultural land, the skilled and affordable workers, the means of transport of goods and the related provisions from other occupations - the pots for growing, the osiers for weaving into packaging and baskets, the availability of farm animals such as horses for carrying goods. It was the right time and place and the demand for horticultural material was strong both from the necessity for growing productive plants for sustenance but also for delight, enquiry and aesthetic satisfaction.

Notes

1   Thomas H. Rivers, *250 Years of Thomas Rivers and Son Ltd. of Sawbridgeworth,* 1975.

2.   *The Story of Sawbridgeworth, Book 1,* p. 25.

3.   *Ibid.,* pp. 10, 19, 26, 29, 30.

4.   Tithe Map and Award 1838 in Hertfordshire Archives and Local Studies.

5.   Pigot and Company, *National Trades Directory,* 1839.

6.   1843 Estate map produced for the sale of the Pishobury Estate, courtesy John Sapsford.

7.   John Harvey, *Early Nurserymen* (London, 1974), pp. 1 - 10.

8.   *The Story of Sawbridgeworth, Book 1,* p. 53.

9.   Malcolm Thick, *The Supply of Seeds, Plants and Trees to the Kitchen Garden and Orchard, 1600-1800',* (London, 1998), p. 37.

10.   Harvey, pp. 90 - 93.

11.   Thick, p 41.

Chapter Three

The Structure of a Horticulture Business

The third Thomas Rivers (1798 - 1877) took over a thriving and well established horticultural business. Despite the lack of any early records, we know something of its structure from Thomas' books and articles, from the horticultural journals of the nineteenth century whose correspondents regularly visited the Sawbridgeworth grounds, and from the oral history gathered from employees and their families about the period from the early twentieth century on. Although the pace of change accelerated especially after WWII, much of the horticultural practice of the earlier twentieth century, still vivid in childhood memories and fathers' tales, followed traditional forms.

When the third Thomas took over the direction of the business in 1837, it was a well established, prosperous and growing company that owned an increasing number of acres. In his writing, he refers to the orchard-like nursery grounds planted by his grandfather where he could wander sampling fruit in all seasons. He relies on a large, stable and skilled workforce. The elements of a successful business were already in place. What was it like?

Although the business reached its maximum size in terms of land ownership at the end of the nineteenth century when the holdings amounted to as much as four hundred acres, it had become much earlier a very important local employer, second only to the malting industry. It had established the organisation required for running a successful nursery - an extent of many acres available for growing, the traditional family employer status with both the sons of the Rivers family owners following their fathers into directing the business, and the sons of the workers following their fathers into employment. There were good transport links for sending stock

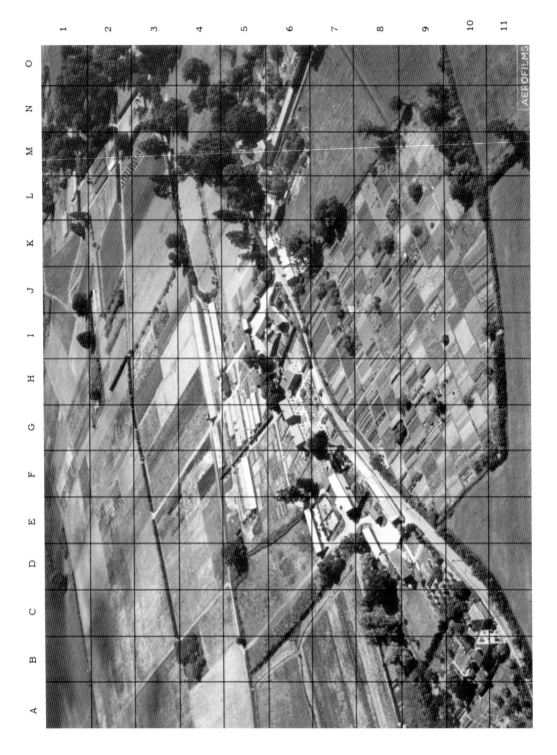

1949 Aerial Photograph showing a large area of the Rivers Nursery property with a key to important structures

M/N 1 — Bonks Hill House, white house in the grove of trees

L1/ M2 — Orchard Houses behind Bonks Hill House

M2 — Citrus House

L2 — Water Tower, behind houses

J1 — Well with pumping mechanism hauled by pony, hidden by trees

I5/ J5 — Wiseman's area, with Office, packing sheds, bell and later Garden Centre

G/H/I/J 4 — Vinery, 300' long

G/I 5, I4 — More glasshouses

E8 — Little Pennys farmyard, stable for horses, later garage for vehicles

D8/9 — Little Pennys farmhouse, used as a residence

A-M 1-6 — Fields for horticulture

F-M 7-10 — Town allotments

B10-11 — Newports

C3-H2 — Beech Hedge

E4-J4 — Line of ditch draining Rivers land

from A11 West to **L5** East — High Wych/ Sawbridgeworth Road

from A6 one field West — Site of Restored Rivers Nursery Orchard

41

to local and distant parts and the traditional activities associated with growing cycles were well established, the knowledge of good practice being passed on from generation to generation.

Land use

In acquiring land for this horticultural business entire farms were taken over with their farm houses and outbuildings. The houses were available both for family and tied housing for employees and the other buildings served different purposes such as stabling for the cart horses and the like. Land was used in a flexible way. From year to year depending on demand different areas were turned over to different uses. In the mid-nineteenth century twenty thousand Early Rivers bare-rooted plums were sent out each autumn, and the fields had to be adjusted to produce this popular crop. If, as Thomas Rivers writes in the *Rose Amateur's Guide*, more acres on the Sawbridgeworth grounds were given to roses than at any other nursery, there had to be space for them. As John Sapsford says, though the business produced plants, never fruit for the markets, if there was fruit available it was not wasted.[1]

So what were the elements of land use? There were beech hedges, some of which survive to this day, planted to shelter the growing area from harsh winds and moderate the cold weather. On the way to developing glasshouses we hear of spaces with beech hedge walls being covered, later with glass, to provide benign growing conditions for tender plants.

There were growing fields, ready to be laid to the young trees being matured to sell as bare rooted stock in the autumn and winter. These were two or three years old and were previously grown on in propagation areas, where they had been budded or grafted onto root stocks if necessary. Depending on what was offered through the catalogues each year room had to be found for all kinds of growing stock.

There were also orchards, mainly to provide stock for budding and grafts. These orchards were used for propagation until no longer in good condition and then a new area was grown on to replace it. As fruit was only sent to market as a by-product, the orchards were only incidentally allowed to mature. John Sapsford remembers an orchard on Redricks Lane, on Rivers land separated from the main area that he recalls as mainly for propagation wood. The restored orchard, now become a Community Orchard on the former Rivers site, was planted following WWII and was used for propagation material and as a show orchard to allow customers to see the potential of fruit stock they were being offered.[2] Because it was never meant as a productive market crop producing orchard it was allowed to deteriorate when no longer needed for propagation stock, accounting for its sad state when first the volunteers took it on.

There was what the third Thomas refers to as a hospital quarter, where unsold or weak stock was set in a fairly random manner while awaiting some other fate. As he found much of his inspiration for new ideas for nurturing and developing new stock there, this became an important area too.

Some of the fields were used for arable crops, particularly when required by government order during WWI and II, but also in between other uses. There were fields of strawberries and other soft fruits. All of these were flexible arrangements responding to the business needs. What seems today set and permanent boundaries were always subject to usage.

The boundary land at the edge of the property was given over at times to attractive floral displays, on the slope where the houses of Burnside now stand.[3]

The osier, or willow, beds were the most distant area of Rivers property bordering the river Stort near Kecksy's Bridge. At the end of the lane down from Three Mile Pond to the river was the railway track and over that the osier bed. As the horse and cart passed the station it was necessary to alert the station master of the proposed trip over the tracks to cut osiers so that trains could be warned. Land girls helped load the bundled osiers into the carts for transport back up to the packing sheds near Wiseman's where the osiers were bent into frames laid on hessian and packed with straw to transport trees to places as distant as India. The land girls of WWII speak of picking the abundant primroses that bloomed in spring in the damp earth of the osier bed. [4]

William Dedman,
c. 1940,
driving a cart loaded
with osiers.
Reproduced by kind permission
of John Sapsford
Figure 3.2

Glasshouses

Over time after the tax on glass was removed in 1845, a series of large glasshouses were erected in two areas, one behind Bonks Hill house which included the Citrus House and another further west, off the High Wych road. There were found the large Vinery and propagation houses, now more or less the site of the Rivers hospital today. Some of these were huge and when cleared offered spaces for gathering workers and their families for entertainments on occasion. Aerial photographs from the 1950s show these glasshouses still standing though by then their condition was deteriorating. These modified and extended the growing season and allowed fruit that would never thrive in the British climate to prosper. All were made from timber with glass plates. Rivers' book, *The Orchard House*, gives exact specifications for creating such a building and its costs in the mid-nineteenth century.

Oranges in the Snow
Reproduced by kind permission of Eric Willison

Figure 3.3

Water supply and irrigation

Water had to be supplied to the growing areas. At the highest point on the land, there was a water tower built up on brick pillars, the tank filled from a well a little distance away. The water was pumped up from the well to the height of the tower by a pony tethered to trudge in circles around the rotary mechanism. From the tower gravity took the water in pipes to the growing areas. This part of the mechanics of growing was still in use in the 1950s.[5]

Equipment

Through the WWII period most work was carried out by traditional hand methods, labour intensive digging and cultivating. Pictures of the land girls showed them in fields with spades and hand tools setting and removing trees or weeding. Even the office girls had to help during very busy periods in the horticultural years: Eileen Tybjerg, who worked in the office from 1968 to 1983, remembered thinning peaches in the glasshouses, necessary to get a crop of good fruit, as being the job she liked least when she was pressed into service.[6]

There was, however, one very interesting machine, now disappeared: a steam plough. Eric Willison remembers that after harvesting the big field would be ploughed up with a steam plough. There was a steam engine with an anchor carriage positioned on the opposite side of the field. A windlass, cable on a drum, enabled the engine to draw the plough backwards and forward across the field. Three men were needed, one for each position across the field and one with the plough. The distance and uneven quality of the land was such that at points the men lost sight of each other, had to shout out when time came to reverse the movement. This piece of equipment was hired, not owned by Rivers Nursery. Even the men working the mechanism came with the machine. Rivers only provided coal and water. One of the same engines would come again in late summer to thresh the corn, using a belt from the engine flywheel to drive the threshing machine.[7]

Methods of transport

Whether carrying people and tools to cultivation areas or transporting goods to market, most of the trips were by horse-drawn vehicles at least until the end of the nineteenth century. The horses were stabled at Little Penny's farm. It was possible to drive a horse and cart not only locally but much further afield, even all the way to London only twenty or twenty-five miles distant. When the railways came in, the carts transported materials to the station and from there by this extensive and efficient system around the country and around the Empire. If at some period the canalised Stort was utilised by the Rivers company, as might have been the case, there is no evidence to substantiate any use of it. Probably for horticultural material river transport was too slow.

Before WWII a small lorry arrived for Nursery use. This was during a period before cars and lorries were commonplace. It was used for various jobs around the Nursery. It was also to transport displays to the horticultural shows. The land girls speak of being trained to use it and the various mishaps that occurred. If the trees were bumped in the process of learning to drive, the scars were soothed they said by applications of 'Rivers ointment' - mud!

Lorry transporting hay to the stack, 1942.

Reproduced by kind permission of Vera Maskell

Figure 3.4

Certainly plants and people travelled from the Rivers Nursery to far-flung places. There is a letter in Kew documenting fruit Kew ordered sent from Rivers in 1887 to the Horticultural Gardens in Lucknow, India. [8]

There was also an advisory service. Well-to-do people purchasing large homes and gardens in Sawbridgeworth were able to request help to identify the existing fruit trees in their orchards. Then managers of the time would lead planting teams to set out more trees, both fruit and ornamental, to fill the gaps in their orchards and gardens. There might have been two or three gangs of men sent out at any one time to large estates to design and plant areas of orchard or forest and ornamental trees in the grounds.[9]

The office

In the office were processed the orders from wherever they arose. Order books that are preserved in the Hertfordshire Archives and Local Studies, list processed orders. All meticulously recorded by hand, with certain symbols for bad debts, these extant pages from the 1930s, 40s, and 50s, record mostly small purchases and have posting addresses all around the country. Probably the larger orders were processed separately and transported by the gangs of men to set them in. Some employees were hired as office girls and their jobs consisted of working with the managers to deal with orders, except at the busiest times in the horticultural year, when help was needed in the glasshouses to thin fruit or perhaps pollinate. Office girls also modeled in the glasshouses with the Rivers daughters for publicity materials, their well groomed hair and pretty faces making good advertisements.

Associated trades and skills

Although Rivers supplied its own needs as far as packing materials, other craftsmen and suppliers provided such materials as pots - by the mid-nineteenth century used in the glasshouses for the miniature trees the third Thomas pioneered and advocated for the general public - and baskets for showing in the horticultural exhibits as well as more everyday uses. The success of the nursery business gave benefits to other trades.

Rivers' book *The Orchard House* gives a list of suppliers: for 'pots - Messrs. Scales, Stoke Newington, London; Glass - Messrs. Phillips & Co, Bishopsgate Without, London; Anticorrsion Paint - Messrs. Carson & Son, London'. Growing in pots was a key element of the development of a tender species culture and the Nursery employed a variety of pots of 18, 15, 13, and 11 inch sizes. Their uses are carefully explained in the book and figure in all the photographs that were later taken in the glasshouses.[10]

Men in front of the packing shed bundling trees for despatch
Reproduced by kind permission of The Herts and Essex Observer, Friday, December 30, 1949

Figure 3. 5

The packing shed

In the packing shed, the plant materials were set up to withstand long journeys by rail and other transport, sometimes to very distant places. With no modern materials of plastic and the like, the packers used what nowadays are seen to be totally sustainable materials, the osiers and straw from the fields. Lengths of osiers cut to size were laid down, shaped and bent to conform to the outlines of the young tree or other plants. Straw used to fill in the spaces, cushion and preserve the damp rootstock - all trees were sent out bare-rooted in the autumn or winter - labeled and driven down to the railway station to be dispatched on their way.

Orders from other nurseries

From the order books that survive we also see another regular cooperative working practice in the horticultural trade: when big orders of certain plants caused shortages, nurseries relied on ordering in quantities of the popular variety from other nurseries. We learn for example that on the ninth of November, 1922, as the country was recovering after WWI, Rivers purchased ten thousand Quick or hawthorn to be sold on for hedging from Wood and Ingram Nursery in Huntingdon. Wood and Ingram in turn stocked Rivers' Early Prolific plum. [11]

Advertising and promotion

As a sophisticated business the Nursery used a whole range of methods to promote their products. From the early nineteenth century catalogues of roses - an early specialism of Rivers Nursery - listed the many roses available to buy, clustering them around the seasons of their flowering and kind. The third Thomas issued his first book, *The Rose Amateur's Guide,* to explore the possibilities of the different roses and the cultural conditions most likely to give the best results. He followed this practice of issuing rather contemplative notes discussing the visions of a breeder with his other two books on aspects of orchard fruit growing. These books served to enhance the reputation of the Nursery, and his own reputation as an outstanding horticulturist. References by name and detail to orders of notable customers - as when the orchard house built for Lord Brayebrooke at Audley End is pictured in one edition - amounts to a canny and subtle advertising practice. While not directly commercial, more practical and scientific explorations, the books must have increased sales from the catalogues that advertised his new discoveries.

In addition to catalogues, there were advertisements in the papers for the company just as there continued to be until the Nursery was sold. The advertisements in the nineteenth century horticultural journals were incidental to the larger effect on reputation and sales of the regular reports of visits to the nursery grounds and descriptions of what could be found growing there by journal correspondents. There were also articles written mostly by the third Thomas Rivers though T. Francis Rivers, his son, also wrote occasionally. From the 1930s there are dramatic professional photographs of the Nursery, often of activities in the glasshouses, taken to accompany press stories about the Nursery (though the stories themselves do not survive), representing a certain glossy kind of advertising.

Another kind of promotion that came along later, from about the early twentieth century, was Rivers' displaying at various horticultural shows - and often receiving prizes. Their medals were noted on the front page of the catalogue, serving again to remind buyers of the excellence of the Rivers stock.

The rhythm of work

The working days that emerged from the practices and structures described belonged to the pattern of working life in a rural community of continuous agricultural traditions. The style of life changed little over the period Rivers Nursery existed. It was not until after WWII that conditions altered rapidly

Pollinating with a paint brush
Reproduced by kind permission of John Sapsford
Figure: 3.6

to become the faster paced, mechanised, mobile existence we see in this urbanized area today.

Into the early twentieth century, most people worked as close to home as possible and walked to their place of employment. The Rivers Nursery was established to the south west of the Sawbridgeworth centre and most people who worked there generally lived nearby in High Wych and on the south side of the town centre. Sons followed fathers in Rivers employ so that often several members of the same family worked there at the same time. People did not generally wear watches and the working day was regulated by the sound of a bell that rang people to work and signaled as well the end of the day. Traditional working practices, having been established, continued.

The Rivers family directors travelled as part of their role, just as many had done in youth to expand their education or seek their fortunes. Observing horticultural practices in other countries led to new ideas. Cultivars were collected from elsewhere, particularly France as names reveal, and brought home to be adapted to English growing conditions. As we see documented in the writing of the third Thomas, he constantly considered how to improve his stock and some different kinds of cultivation were established. But generally these were fitted into the long established ways. Expertise was handed down through the generations, the older workers showing the newcomers how to go about propagating and nurturing plants. Some who eventually took more managerial roles had training in agricultural colleges or centres like Wisley during the twentieth century before coming to Rivers to learn side by side with the general workers before taking up better paid posts. Rivers was recommended by the Ministry of Agriculture in the twentieth century to aspiring horticulturists here and from abroad. John Sapsford speaks of students sent from various countries to learn the trade, an Austrian in particular who worked with his father Arthur and who suggested that he should come to Austria to take up work.

For the workers it was a slow-paced, stable way of life. Most general staff were paid the usual low agricultural wages, but it seems that the work was more pleasant than working on a farm and something that people would choose to follow their families into rather than choose to work in a factory or farm or malting. The workforce for horticultural tasks was predominantly male until the world wars.

During WWI when the Women's Land Army was first established, at a time when supplies were short in Britain, more food had to be rapidly produced to feed the country. Many men were gone to war and women were conscripted to take their places. Rivers Nursery was required by the government to grow some food crops on land usually given to horticulture. There was probably a much smaller number of women and more limited use of land for food during WWI than later from 1939, when more women came, more food crops were grown and even the Rivers family seat, Bonks Hill house, was taken over by the Army. By that time, there were already women working on the land, and some recall that when some land army girls joined them, they were paid a higher wage and given a uniform. [12]

Many people speak of their working life at Rivers as being very happy. The tasks were predictable, following the horticultural year, and there was an easy, cheerful companionship that many speak of. There was of course also opportunity for flirtation and courtships, rivalry and disappointments. There is the dramatic story of one of the managers committing suicide due, as rumour has it, to an unhappy love affair. The women particularly when they arrived in the twentieth century found a freedom there that was lacking in other work or even in their lives at home. All but a very few left school at fourteen, and were then immediately thrust into work by their families, which with many other children at home, needed both space and extra income. They went into domestic or shop work, often living in and seldom free even to visit their families. By contrast the better conditions and easy comradeship of working at Rivers must have seemed good. Kath Walsh, who came to Rivers during WWII and stayed on for forty years becoming the last Tom Rivers' chief propagator - in contrast to most who left when they married and had children - says 'they were the happiest days of my life'.[13]

The relationship between the Rivers family and their employees, whatever it might have been in the earlier times, had become by the nineteenth century and into the twentieth more that of a beneficent gentleman owner and his employees. Edith Brace, many of whose relatives worked at Rivers over the years speaks of curtseying as a child to the family members, the men doffing their hats.[14] There was a well established hierarchy among the working staff as well, with the clothes people wore reflecting their status, for example bowler hats for managers, flat caps for workers. But if the times required deference, there was also the sense of security in working for a long-established firm expected to continue indefinitely, a relationship of trust between the owner directors through the time of the last Thomas Rivers who died in 1978 and the people they worked with every day. Some employees lived in tied houses - the housing that had in some cases come with the purchase of land - and were promised life tenancy, just as other houses were occupied by family members on a long-term basis whether they worked for the Nursery or not. People were cared for in times of need and though there was no formal government pension or welfare system for most of the Rivers period, a good employer cared for his long-term staff into their old age. There were also some outings laid on for staff, summer trips to the seaside and such and a dinner and entertainment in winter. If there were what seem hardships to the modern sensibility there was also a quiet rhythm and security that could be counted on to continue.

Notes

1. John Sapsford, Recorded Interview, 27 April 2009.
2. Nina Elsdon, Interview, 23 January 2009.
3. Tup Armes, Recorded Interview, 18 March 2009.
4. *Ibid.*
5. John Sapsford.
6. Eileen Tybjerg Interview, *18 May 2007.*
7. John Sapsford. Eric Willison, Recorded Interview, 16 April 2009.
8. Note to W.T. Thiselton Dyer from Rivers Nursery, Jan. 14, 1887. Kew Archives.
9. John Sapsford.
10. Thomas Rivers, *The Orchard-House or the Cultivation of Fruit-trees under Glass,* fourteenth edition (London, 1870), p. 50.
11. John Drake, *Wood & Ingram, A Huntingdonshire Nursery 1742 - 1950* (Huntingdon, 2008), pp. 121, 149.
12. Nina Elsdon.
13. Kath Walsh Martin, Interview, 13 April, 2009.
14. Edith Brace, Interview, 28 February, 2007.

Chapter Four
Positions, Responsibilities, Status and Day-to-day Work: Employees' Tales

By talking to all those we could find who themselves worked at the Nursery or who had family employed at Rivers, we have accumulated in our Archives a rich store of memories that stretch back to the early twentieth century. There is a sense of the traditional working ways continuing, largely unchanged, until the post WWII era when the upheaval in the rural way of life affected employment in Sawbridgeworth. As the pay and the expectations of working people increased, as the former markets for Rivers Nursery horticultural products declined, as land was sold and new houses covered previously farmed acres, as car ownership increased and commuting began, the old ways at Rivers changed and in an attempt to save the company, a modern garden centre was set up to run alongside the catalogue sales. When the Nursery did not succeed with the new venture and the business and all the remaining acres were sold, the Rivers era passed into history.

However, it is possible from listening to people to see how it used to be and to gain a sense of its purposeful activity that seemed both rewarding and secure. The Nursery had been there forever; the company would always be there as it had always been. There would always be fields to cultivate, glasshouses and stock to nurture. The family directors valued their workforce and it seems generally acknowledged that the employees were treated with respect and care was taken for their welfare so that there was a good working atmosphere. People often say that their working lives there were 'happy days'. There was a hierarchical structure of employment, with most of the casual workers receiving low pay on a par with agricultural labour, although the horticultural work was considered more congenial than farm work it seems. Those in charge of the labourers - the managers and foremen - were the people who made the creative advances of thinkers like the third Thomas (1798 - 1877) become realities. Rivers' ideas that resulted in the development of new varieties and the implementation of new methods of growing and nurturing plants were carried out through their efforts, to be judged successful and incorporated into the usual routines or rejected as failures.

Foremen

Directly in charge of the working people were the foremen. At the height of the business there were a number of foremen, for the glasshouse complex behind Bonks Hill house, for the glasshouses at Wisemans, and for planting outside. Josh Brace was orchard house foreman from 1882. He had worked with the developer of the orchard house, the third Thomas, so must have been an employee at the nursery long before becoming foreman as would have been usual. Brace carried out in practical terms the theory Rivers was developing as is known from the book that Brace wrote: *The Culture of Fruit Trees in Pots*, published in 1904. Brace writes in the preface: 'My chief aim in writing this book is to lay down the rules of management of fruit trees in pots, which from a lifelong experience, I have found essential to success. I have avoided theory as much as possible and confined myself to the advocacy of what is simple, practical and useful...'[1]

Edith Brace, grand-niece of Josh, ninety years old at the time of describing him, tells of his walking past her door at 13 London Rd. where she had lived all her life, on the way up to the Nursery every day, summoned by the bell that rang workers in at 7.30am. In summer he wore, she said, his straw boater and sack apron and in winter a black derby hat and black apron, replaced by hessian once at work. His outfit indicates his status as foreman and is in contrast to the clothes and flat hats of the working men. In figure 4.2 we see on the end of the first row a young lad. Boys might begin working at the Nursery at age fourteen immediately after leaving school and continue long past present day retirement age as the pension system in place today was not fully developed. [2]

Josh Brace
Reproduced by kind permission
of Eric Willison
Figure 4.1

**Josh Brace with a
working team**
Reproduced by kind permission
of John Sapsford
Figure 4.2

To be a foreman was to have a position of responsibility that came with
having learned horticultural skills from previous generations of workers,
there being no usual academic training until later in the twentieth century.
The responsibility included working with the family directors to put theory
into practice and training the working staff. As glasshouse foreman, it was
also Brace's responsibility to safeguard the plants in winter cold and summer
heat.

Brace's preface comments: 'The protection afforded by glass was at first
thought sufficient to keep out all frost but, as time went on, it was deemed
advisable to make assurance doubly sure by using a little artificial heat in the

event of a severe frost.'[3] Using a little heat involved a lot of work for the foreman. More of this particular responsibility is learned from the family of Joe Stubbings who is pictured in other photographs at the beginning of his time at Rivers as one of the working men posing with Josh Brace. Both his son, Walter Stubbings, and his daughter, Tup Stubbings Armes, have contributed stories about their father at Rivers and his working life. [4]

Joe Stubbings in the
Orange House
Reproduced by kind permission
of John Sapsford

Figure 4.3

Martin Stubbings, known as Joe, and his family also lived very close to the Nursery on London Rd near the Brace family. As Edith Brace said, over the years many of the houses on that end of London Rd. were lived in by Rivers employees and the children played up in the Rivers fields behind their houses. Joe had worked at the Nursery pre-WWI and when he returned took up his employment there again, eventually becoming foreman. Despite a bad leg injury suffered in the war, part of his responsibility as recalled by his daughter was to go up the glasshouses every single day including weekends and even Christmas, to fire the boilers with coal ensuring that the heat for the delicate fruit never failed.

Among his other responsibilities were to supervise the propagation of thousands of cuttings and the packing of bare-rooted trees to send out. He also went to all the horticultural shows.

That these foremen were knowledgeable as well as dedicated and capable men is evident, even if their formal education had been scant. As for Joe, women in the war years workforce called him 'the professor' as he 'went on about many things'. [5]

Walter Stubbings, Joe's son, also came to work at Rivers when he left school at fourteen in 1934. He continued to work there until joining the RAF in WWII and then returned for another ten years after the war before going on to horticultural employment elsewhere in the area.

The horticultural year

Walter writes interestingly about the ordinary seasonal routines as experienced by the general workforce:

The department I started in was the glasshouses behind Bonks Hill House. The larger iron frame green house was near to Bonks Hill House. This contained fan-trained orange, lemon and grapefruit trees pictured in some newspapers. The smaller one contained apples and pears in pots. Other orchard houses contained plums and cherries in one, peaches and nectarines in another. These trees were grown in larger pots and mainly used for fruiting and show purposes. Another glasshouse was used for tomato growing in summer and cleared for potting autumn and winter.

As the seasons went on the large cherry trees in the orchard house ripened early. The fruit was cut off and packed in square boxes in layers and sent to market. Meanwhile the peaches and nectarines together with the other fruit trees in pots were top-dressed with rotted farmyard manure to feed and help to retain moisture in the hot summers. Early mornings trees were sprayed with water by syringe to create a good growing atmosphere and to check red spider and other pests. Late afternoon the houses were damped down on hot days. The fan-trained peaches and nectarines also received the same treatment.

The citrus trees were potted in different types of soil. They were fed by liquid feed during the growing period from a tank filled with water in which farmyard manure and bags of soot were put and left to soak. The liquid later taken out and used to feed. Meanwhile out in the nursery young fruit stocks were being budded and trained trees were being tied out on frames of canes to make espalier and fan trained trees for sale.

At this time new soil and turf was being stacked up ready for potting later in the season. As the seasons passed the peaches and nectarines

**Walter Stubbings
repotting trees**
Reproduced by kind permission
of *Amateur Gardening* Magazine

Figure 4.4

were picked and packed in wooden boxes containing woodwool [fine wood shavings] for markets. Also plums in the orchards were packed in wicker baskets.

During the summer and autumn months pot fruit trees from the orchard houses together with trees and grapevines were selected from the other greenhouses at the High Wych road site for exhibition at various flower shows including Chelsea, York and Shrewsbury, together with local shows .

As autumn approached the greenhouses were all tidied up after leaf fall. Young fruit trees in pots were sent for orders and packing at the High Wych Road site. With autumn approaching, fruit picking was in full swing. Apples and pears were placed in the fruit shed. This was a brick built building with a thatched roof. Inside were 3 tier shelves the bottom two were for storage The top shelves were laid out with samples of all varieties grown for reference to customers needs and nursery work and shows. The rest were sent in the baskets to markets.

Autumn was also time for repotting the trees in pots. Also trees were brought in from the nursery for replacements. Fruit stocks that had been budded the previous summer were potted on and grown on for trees for sale in later years. The potting programme was that a greenhouse was taken over. Soil was taken in from the soil stacked in the previous summer by horse and cart. This was mixed with old plaster and farmyard manure and malt dust from the Maltings. The pots were washed and recrocked for drainage. So the year ended.

Walter Stubbings, March, 2009

Women in the workforce

Although it was usual for women to work in the office, dealing with orders and keeping the books, women did not work on the land. During WWI as there was a shortage of food supplies to feed the civilian population, the Nursery was required to set aside some of the horticultural work in order to grow crops. At that time, there may have been women conscripted for field work on Rivers land.

Certainly during WWII it was an accepted practice for women to fill the gaps in the workforce. The men who remained at the Nursery were in a reserved occupation or too old to go to war. The government conscripted single women aged between twenty and thirty. According to the women who have spoken of those times, there was a choice in the Sawbridgeworth area between working on local farms or in factories nearby producing war materials and working at Rivers. Work at Rivers was often considered preferable and for those who were local, much closer. Some of those who came to Rivers were in the Land Army, which meant that they had uniforms and somewhat better pay. Other women who had already been employed to work on the land did not have uniforms, but all did the same work under the direction of foremen.[6]

It seems from the tales told that the work was sometimes dirty - an example given is the usual practice of top dressing pots with manure without using gloves - and at times hard - the digging in the fields. But the women generally had a good time. They were young, lively, even playful, chatty, ready to laugh. The work offered opportunities for fun. For them, there was a sense of freedom from the traditional domestic round of ordinary household or shop work or of caring for the numerous members of an extended family all living in very close quarters as is often described. It sounds as though the foremen had their hands full.

Tribute must be paid to these women who were suddenly thrust into a man's world that had formerly been closed to them and expected to do the same jobs to the same standards. Their delight in the freedom found and the good humour they brought to their work as well as the work they successfully completed is quite remarkable. It is not to be forgotten that they opened doors for all women to follow into more fulfilling work with fewer conventional restraints than before.

Land girls with sheaves of harvested corn
Reproduced by kind permission of Vera Maskell
Figure 4.5

The war was going on around them. The army had taken over Bonks Hill House. Errands and walking up the paths beside the house to the Nursery grounds brought the girls into contact with army personnel. More dramatic, one day as Nina Elsdon describes, 'we looked up from digging in the fields to see wave after wave of flights of bombers towing gliders pass overhead' - maybe, she thinks, that was for the battle of Arnhem.[7] But memories focus on the companionship of everyday life. Vera Maskell remembers 'mucking about', as does Nina. Nina speaks of its being a 'wonderful life'. Vera remembers being trained to drive the lorry and bumping into trees and fixing the scrapes with *'Rivers ointment'* - mud.[8]

After the war when the men returned to the workforce, the women working on the land went back to their domestic roles or other kinds of employment.

Office Girls

The girls working in the office had a cleaner but more routine life. Women like Eileen Tybjerg recorded in meticulous handwriting the details of orders. She came to work in the office in 1968, staying until 1983. She said there were then as many as a dozen office staff. She eventually became head office girl and came to live at 54 Wiseman's Cottage, almost next door to her office. Wiseman's was at that time a Rivers property rented to employees. She was very happy in her job and enjoyed working for the last Thomas Rivers, describing him as a kind man who had 'such feelings for the nursery'. The only task she didn't like was thinning peaches in the glasshouse in order that there would be bigger, showier crops for displays; all staff were drawn into horticultural tasks at peak times.[9]

Office girls were also chosen to pose for publicity photos as were the Rivers family daughters, their pretty faces showing up well among the plants in the glasshouses, even though they had not helped with the cultivation.

Kitty Church, who worked in the office, photographed in a glasshouse
Reproduced by kind permission of John Sapsford
Figure 4.6

Managers

The general manager of the nursery was a very important figure. It was he who directed the day to day operations. The manager ensured the smooth running of the business even when the family director was absent, perhaps away travelling to see other growers at work here or abroad, giving talks at horticultural gatherings and the like. The manager was also there running the business in interim periods when changes in family directors were taking place. Many managers' names come up in employees' stories but there are two - William Camp and Arthur Sapsford - whose direct descendants have knowledge of the contributions they made to the firm.

William Camp was born in 1847 into a long established local family, shoemakers for two generations. An article in the *Gardeners' Chronicle* written about him at the time of his retirement in 1926 at age seventy nine, records some of his achievements. He came into Rivers employ during the time of the third Thomas and his aptitude was apparently quickly recognised as after seven years there, he was taken on as a clerk by Veitch Nurseries of Chelsea, the most renowned horticulture business of the time. He stayed there only two years before coming back to Rivers as chief clerk, a high position for someone aged only twenty-four. Ten years later, he returned to Veitch, and while working there for another period observed the excitement generated by great horticulture and the enthusiasm of royal visitors and many others to the grounds. He also learned of the importance of displaying at horticultural shows. When he later came back to work for Thomas Frances Rivers as manager, he developed that side of the business and led the Nursery to successes in winning prizes at many important shows, further enhancing the reputation of the company.[10]

He was rewarded well for his work, living in Newports, a substantial home, on the High Wych Rd near the Nursery. His son and grandson continued to work at the Nursery. William Camp was also prominent in local society, becoming one of the first Church wardens of the newly built High Wych Church.

Arthur Sapsford became general manager of the Nursery in 1936. The first Sapsford family contact with the Rivers was when Arthur's mother became housekeeper for the bachelor Henry S. Rivers in 1903, who lived in Little Pennys, a house customarily used by the second son in the family. When Arthur left school in 1911, he started a job as office boy at Rivers. During WWI he was in France for three or four years, coming back to Rivers, marrying and going to live with his wife in Gilders farmhouse, another Rivers property, where his son John was born. Arthur soon became a glasshouse foreman and later manager.

William Camp in a glasshouse
Reproduced by kind permission of Eric Willison

Figure 4.7

His responsibilities included the now customary preparation for display and exhibition in horticultural shows where Rivers continued to win awards. His son John went with him at times as a boy and speaks of driving there in the Nursery lorry loaded with display plants and of the excitement of the show itself.

As had previous managers, Arthur went out to big or important customers to advise on planting layouts and choice of shrubberies, large trees and fruit areas. He also organised gangs of Rivers workers to plant up the designs. Different teams might be working at a number of locations at

Arthur Sapsford receiving a prize at a show, probably Windsor, being careful not to fall off the stage
Reproduced by kind permission of John Sapsford

Figure 4.8

any one time. Eventually Arthur moved with his family to Weeping Ash bungalow, traditionally the general manager's house, very near to the glasshouses behind Bonks Hill. John Sapsford recalls the really lovely environment inside the glasshouses, especially the citrus house, where fragrant flowers continued on the trees even while the oranges ripened. As Arthur was maintaining the best conditions to prepare trees for the shows, he too had to go over to the glasshouses at weekends to check on the boilers.

After WWII the big estates were much reduced so that for Rivers too a decline in business continued. The workforce numbers, more or less stable up to this time, were reduced. Arthur Sapsford eventually left Rivers employ and went to work at the Riches Ironmonger's Store. At the time of his leaving Rivers he built a bungalow for himself and the family on Brook Lane, in an area Rivers had owned.[11]

As in any workplace, around the work were the friendships and hostilities, the excitement of flirtations and liaisons, the

A Rivers horticultural show display, perhaps Southport

Reproduced by kind permission of John Sapsford

Figure 4.9

marriage partners first encountered in the Nursery. There are also tales of relationships that failed and a suicide. Both women and men speak of these episodes but are careful to keep the details to themselves.

Notes

1. Josh Brace, *The Culture of Fruit Trees in Pots* (1904), Preface.
2. Edith Brace. Eric Willison, Recorded Interview, 16 April 2009. John Sapsford.
3. Brace, Preface.
4. Tup Armes. Walter Stubbings, Recorded Interview, 4 February 2009.
5. Nina Elsdon.
6. *Ibid.*
7. *Ibid.*
8. Vera Maskell, Recorded Interview, 18 April 2009.
9. Eileen Tybjerg.
10. 'William Camp', *Gardeners' Chronicle,* March 20, 1926, p. 204.
    Eric Willison, Recorded Interview, 16 April 2009.
11. John Sapsford.

Rootstocks
by Denis Todhunter

Most fruit trees grown today consist of two portions joined together by budding or grafting - i.e. the variety on a rootstock. On the other hand bush fruits, cane fruits, grapes, figs etc are usually on their own root systems.

Many of the varieties of fruit we grow today were originally chance seedlings - i.e. sprung up on their own roots. In due course they all became fruitful but sometimes there was a long wait. The well-known 'Cox's Orange Pippin' was raised from a pip of the 'Ribston Pippin' by a Mr. Cox near Slough and was planted up by commercial growers from about 1850. The best known culinary apple 'Bramley's Seedling' was raised from a pip in Nottinghamshire and was introduced about 1875. 'Conference' pear was raised from a pip by T. F. Rivers and introduced in 1888 with the name of the International Fruit Conference he chaired.

From the foregoing it will be seen that seedling fruit trees do come into being in due course. However, commercial growers require early cropping and a known performance; hence it is standard practice to plant trees on a chosen rootstock.

Fruit tree nurserymen raise rootstocks in vast numbers in stoolbeds or layerbeds but this is quite a costly process and more recently the trend has been increasingly to resort to production from cuttings. After the rootstock cuttings have been planted out and are well-established, they are ready for budding or grafting and after another year or two they are saleable to the fruit grower. The choice of rootstock governs mainly the size of tree and cropping potential. For instance apple rootstocks have been divided into four groups: very dwarfing, semi-dwarfing, vigorous and very vigorous. Much of the pioneer sorting out was carried out by East Malling Research Station in Kent and the stocks were given the prefix Malling or M for short, e.g. MIX (note the use of Roman numerals). Further stocks were introduced following cooperation with John Innes Research Station which at the time was at Merton. These were known as Malling/Merton or MM for short, e.g. MM106. Frequently the stocks were referred to as type e.g. type IX or type XVI.

Variety, soil and spacing are all factors which have to be taken into account when choosing stocks. Many farms planted up in the 1930s had most of their trees on MXIII, a stock which turned out to be very disappointing especially for 'Cox'. At one stage XVI was favoured particularly on light soils where rainfall was low, but nowadays planting fruit on marginal soils is not a proposition.

1960 was an exceptionally wet year and the following spring it was evident that literally thousands of apple trees were very distressed, in fact many were dead or dying. Trees on the dwarfing stock MIX, however, were largely unaffected. Seabrooks of Boreham, Essex consistently favoured MII and the majority of trees they supplied were on this stock.

Today the most popular apple stocks are probably the medium vigorous MM106, the dwarfing M26 and the very dwarfing MIX which has very brittle roots and requires permanent staking. M26 will also require staking for the first four or five years. Pears are usually worked on quince stocks - either Quince A or the more dwarfing Quince C. Common Plum used to be a popular stock for many varieties of plum but nowadays St. Julien A is more commonly used or Pixy for very small trees. St. Julien A is also suitable for peaches and nectarines. In the past sweet cherries were usually grafted on the wild gean but this resulted in a very large trees. Nowadays the semi-dwarfing colt stock is generally used.

An ability to identify rootstocks has sometimes been an advantage in advisory work in the orchard. There was a well-known case on an Essex fruit farm many years ago where a dwarf pyramid apple orchard seemed exceptionally vigorous and the grower despaired of the trees ever becoming fruitful. They were supposedly on a semi-dwarfing rootstock but it was noticed that suckers springing up around some of the trees resembled the rootstocks MM104 which was known to form exceptionally vigorous stock. Specimen shoots were sent to Mr. R. J. Garner at East Malling and he confirmed that they were in fact MM104. The grower realised that at such a close spacing it would be impossible for this ever to be a profitable orchard and all the trees were grubbed and the grower compensated.

In the 1950s, the Ministry of Agriculture introduced the Fruit Tree Rootstocks Certification Scheme to ensure a supply of reliable healthy planting material for the industry. Members of the Ministry's advisory service carried out the nursery inspections usually in August/September and approved stocks had to be true to name, in good health, free from pests and disease and reasonably vigorous. All inspectors were required to go on an annual refresher course at East Malling Research Station.

I think my main memory of inspecting at Rivers Nursery was having finished the job and being invited into the office to have a cup of tea and a chat with Mr. Rivers.

Denis Todhunter had a period of practical experience at Rivers Nursery in the 1940s before attending Reading University. Later, he was employed by the Ministry of Agriculture's advisory service for nearly forty years based in Colchester, Essex, specialising in fruit crops. He visited Rivers annually during the 1960s and 1970s to inspect fruit tree root stocks and blackcurrants. His last visit was in 1981.

Propagation
by Tony Slingsby

> It is…on the discovery of grafting that much of the subsequent history of the domestic apple depends. It gave growers the ability not only to reproduce any useful tree and establish valued varieties elsewhere, but also to transform an otherwise worthless tree. Grafting was a show-case for the gardener's skills, and expertise in grafting has ensured that the best varieties have been conserved for centuries and that we can still grow apples enjoyed by our ancestors.
>
> Joan Morgan and Alison Richards, The Book of Apples (London, 1993)

By the time I was working at the Rivers Nursery, early 1970s, the main difference between propagation on the site as it had been and as it was at the time was that much of the fruit was by then being produced by a wholesale nursery in Worcestershire. As Mr. T.H. Rivers explained in the short pamphlet he wrote on the occasion of the Nursery's two hundred and fiftieth anniversary, virtually all research had been taken over by the research stations of East Malling and Long Ashton. With new emphasis on virus-free trees being the trend, the facilities and quite possibly the necessary skills were no longer readily available at Sawbridgeworth. The orchard which the Rivers Nursery Site Group are working so splendidly to restore ceased to be the source of budwood, since the trees were quite old and not in sufficient isolation to ensure freedom from virus. So the following fruit trees were bought in from the wholesale nursery - apples, pears, plums, apricots, peaches and nectarines, cherries, medlars, quinces, mulberries and all related species.

These plants arrived at Sawbridgeworth in late autumn/early winter, were heeled into prepared troughs in the open ground, and pulled up singly as required for orders throughout the dormant season. Those surplus to requirement for that season's orders would be planted out at the end of the dormant season and grown on for another year. This system applied also to decorative trees, and had the advantage that during the growing season prospective customers could wander round the fields and see in active growth the tree that they might receive totally leafless the following winter!

Kath Walsh Propagator

Reproduced by kind permission of Hertfordshire Archives and Local Studies

(D/ERs/B90/115)

Figure S.1

However, a fair amount of propagation was still taking places. For a start, all the vines and figs were produced from stock plants on the Nursery. This was the undisputed realm of Kath Walsh Martin, who I believe worked here most of her life. With just one or two helpers she raised hundreds of vines and figs each year in an intriguing prop-house which was half sunk into the ground, presumably for heat retention. Into the raised beds of compost on either side, under which I seem to recall there were old cast-iron pipes heated from a boiler at the far end, Kath inserted cuttings of each variety of vine and fig. This material came from the old vinery and another glasshouse in which were grown mature fig trees. As soon as the large old vines became dormant all growth was trimmed off, just leaving the central rod, and these trimmings were stored in a cool frost-free environment until required to be cut into short lengths for use as cuttings. In addition to raising these two fruit types, Kath also grew from grapefruit pips, obtained in bulk from a contact in South Africa, all the rootstocks which were used for propagating the citrus fruit plants.

Before going into details of production of citrus plants, it might help those not conversant with the term to briefly explain the concept of stocks - rootstocks or understocks as they are also known. Although many plants are able to reproduce from seed only a proportion

will be true to type, and some will vary in vigour, i.e. the height to which they will grow when mature. Many years ago it was recognised that budding or grafting on to a related species propagated from cuttings would produce much more uniform results. Thus it was possible to produce fruit trees which would all grow to roughly the same height (depending on the stock chosen), a great advantage for orchard management. Similarly, a bed of roses of the same variety grown on a common stock would look much more attractive than if there were considerable variation in vigour.

So, back to the citrus fruit. Due to the onset of WWII when fuel for heating glasshouses was severely restricted, much of the Rivers collection was lost. About ten stock plants of individual varieties were saved, either planted down the centre of the glasshouses or in large clay pots. This house was one of the few still equipped with heating to get the plants through an English winter. It also had an overhead spray line to keep up the humidity - essential for these plants. Propagation was always done by grafting - by the time I was there anyway - and this involved slicing off the top of the grape fruit stock at an angle and attaching a short cutting taken from the parent plant, cut at a matching

Citrus cuttings 1953

Reproduced by kind permission

of *Amateur Gardening* Magazine

Figure S.3

angle. A small notch in each cut surface produced a 'tongue' and when these were locked together it added stability to the join. This is known as 'whip and tongue' grafting and was the most commonly used method. It does however depend on approximately equal diameters of stock and cutting, and where this was not the case other methods were used, such as 'saddle' or crown' grafting. The junction of the two was then securely wrapped to exclude moisture and infection. A union between the two, stock and cutting (or scion) varied in time but was usually achieved in a couple of months.

Rose production again employed the use of stocks - rosa canina or latterly rosa laxa for bushes and climbers, and rosa rugosa for standards. These arrived from a specialist nursery during the dormant season and were planted up in the open ground. Naturally the practice of rotation of crops was followed with these as for all the open ground production. Once they were established they could be budded using the flowering bushes from the previous year's production. The first step was to carefully hoe away the soil at or slightly below ground level. The foreman would then collect from the previous year's plants sufficient flowering shoots from which the dormant buds would be taken. Those staff trained in budding would then insert the buds into the stocks, followed by others who wrapped the budded area on each plant with a specially designed patch.

The budding knife has a small very sharp blade at one end and a type of spatula at the other. A T-shaped cut was made in the stem of the stock and the flanges opened with spatula. Intro this was inserted a dormant bud from the flowered sticks, but great care was required as it was necessary to first remove the small shield of wood behind the bud.

Figure S.4

Failure to do so would usually result in a failure to bond. During the growing season the budwood patch would attach itself to the stock, and the following spring the head of the stock was cut off, allowing the budded variety to take over. Standards were produced the same way except that three buds were inserted higher up the rosa rugosa stock. We were occasionally asked to insert buds of three different varieties on to a single stock to produce an unusual standard, but this rarely succeeded as the strongest variety usually took over.

Though probably best known for producing top fruit, i.e. apples, pears etc., Rivers sold large quantities of soft fruit - berries and currants. Blackberries, loganberries, strawberries and raspberries were bought in from certified growers. Certification ensured that they were true to variety and healthy, which would not have been easy to guarantee on a mixed nursery like that at Sawbridgeworth. However, all the currants, black, white and red and most of the gooseberries were propagated from cuttings taken near the end of the growing season from mature plants which would later be sold. These plants were checked each year by an inspector from the Ministry of Agriculture. Mr. Todhunter was a very conscientious but charming man, who kept us up to the mark year after year!

In front of one of the glasshouses an enclosed area was constructed with railway sleepers and filled with a peat/sand mix into which the cuttings were inserted. When this bed was filled it was covered with clear polythene to keep in the moisture and by the spring most if not all would have sufficiently rooted to be lined out in one of the fields. Many of the shrubs and hedging plants were treated in the same way, but the success rate was considerably lower. When I was training at Oaklands College in St. Albans I had seen large quantities of the more delicate shrubs raised from soft tip cuttings on benches with undersoil heating and misting equipment. When made responsible for improving shrub production, I requested such facilities, but sadly the funds were not readily available. So we continued to produce what we could by the method described above, and bought in the rest from recognised shrub growers.

That just about covers the bulk of propagation undertaken on the Nursery, though there are one or two less common methods worth mentioning. Though walnuts came from a specialised grower, all the cobnuts and filberts were raised from mature plants by layering. Each year one or two of these large clumps of nuts were stooled, i.e. cut off almost level with the ground. The one year old growths which arose from these stools were bent down and secured to the ground with pegs, a little soil drawn over them, and then left to form their own root system. A similar process was used on some mature tree peonies, though the rooting was much less reliable.

Finally, a method which was a real challenge. Growing in the middle of one of the glasshouses used for young potted fig trees was a splendid Magnolia grandiflora 'Exmouth', and on this we used to practise 'air-layering' or marcotting'. Clean young shoots were selected and slightly wounded, either by making an upward cut about two inches long or ringing the bark. The wound was dusted with hormone growth powder and then a handful of damp sphagnum moss enclosed in polythene film secured above and below the wound, to keep the moisture in. Usually a stout cane was pushed into the ground and the treated shoot secured to this for support. Production of roots within the 'bandage' could take anything form three to twelve months, but when it did the sense of achievement was huge!

The matter of how many of any one variety of plant to propagate was dealt with by careful record keeping of previous years' sales. Nowadays this information would all be stored on computer, but in the 1970s we were still using an old Cardex system. The figures produced by the foreman's annual stock were entered on this and the totals reduced as each incoming order was processed or stock moved from the general holding area into the Garden Centre. When the stock figure of any particular plant became dangerously low, this indicated that we should try to propagate more the following year, and might have to seek stock elsewhere for the current season's orders.

One indication of how plants were increased in earlier years became apparent when I explored some old buildings known as the pigsties - presumably once active in that capacity. There were thousands of tiny clay pots which Mr. Rivers told me were once used to propagate strawberries by sinking them round mature plants and pinning one runner into each pot to root. I am not sure of the modern method of strawberry plant production, but I doubt whether it is quite so labour intensive!

Tony Slingsby worked at Rivers Nursery from 1973 - 1982, progressing from work experience to being manager. He worked with the last Thomas Rivers and after he died in 1978, with Margaret Peeters, the last managing director.

Chapter Five
Thomas Rivers and the Art of Practical Pomology

By the death of Thomas Rivers, of Sawbridgeworth, British Horticulturists lose one of the greatest of experimental physiologists, as well as one of the greatest practical benefactors to their craft. Rose growers, fruit lovers, planters in particular, may revere his memory. A keen man of business, he was yet so imbued with the love of truth for its own sake that, though never neglecting the main chance, he has by his genuine enthusiasm, as well as by the systematic method which guided his proceedings, earned a high place among the small band of vegetable physiologists.[1]

Brought up among a generation quickening with the new impulses communicated to it by the new science and the new politics, the prophet of modern fruit culture was gradually moulded to his work…[2]

Thomas Rivers, 1798 - 1877, the third Thomas in the Rivers Nursery history, was not only the most renowned scientist of the family, experimenting with all aspects of horticulture and the development of new strains, he was also the most prolific writer. Although it is noted both in his own writing and in the pages of the great nineteenth century gardening journals that he kept meticulous notes on his trials of various kinds, none of those notes have survived. Therefore it is fortunate that we can read his three books - *The Rose Amateur's Guide, The Miniature Fruit Garden* and *The Orchard House,* each very popular in its own time and running to as many as eighteen editions. Moreover, his own articles and the commentaries of others visiting him at the Sawbridgeworth Nursery grounds published in the journals provide additional knowledge of his working methods and his day to day interests. His writing has a down-to-earth conversational style and records his considered advances, his failures and his trial methods.

To understand his achievement we must take account of the demands that had to be met to keep his business going. There was the necessity to meet the changing demands of the market, that is the demands of both the grand estates and the smaller householders, to organise the staff and growing areas, and to establish a reputation in the local and wider commercial world.

Modern garden centres largely choose from growers who bring in the new varieties created by specialists, pot up, pass on and serve the demands of the commerce side of choice by providing a pleasant place to tempt customers. However, the nineteenth century nursery businesses dealt with development of new strains as well as with propagation and nurture, including finding root stocks and systems of shelter and soil that would bring the plants in English conditions to their highest quality. Thus Thomas Rivers was not just to be the purveyor of plants but the dreamer of beauty and the creator of prototypes. All of these functions were united under the one banner. Those scientific explorations now given to specialists were the domain of regional nurseries and the better they were at such development the more their reputation spread and the business gained profit. The search for new varieties involved trips abroad to seek out new stock to bring home to adapt to local weather and soil or to gain inspiration by looking at and discussing developments elsewhere.

Although there were certainly these processes taking place at the Thomas Rivers Nursery in the first century of the business - as it grew and established itself in the region, went from renting land to buying it and more of it, establishing its name and attracting a loyal workforce, laying down the foundations of a successful business - little is known of the process itself as there are no records. Our understanding of the dreams of growers changes with the third Thomas Rivers. He was a prolific writer, producing not only the catalogues which by that period nurseries commonly issued but three books designed 'for the horticultural amateur' and a continuous stream of articles in horticultural journals.

Thomas Rivers at his desk,
pen in hand Reproduced from the
Journal of Horticulture and
Cottage Gardener, March 9, 1899

Figure 5.1

These journals, established by renowned horticulturists as places of enquiry, suited the exchange of ideas. The first devoted only to horticulture was established by John Loudon in 1826, *The Gardener's Magazine,* and *The Gardeners' Chronicle* was founded in 1841 by Joseph Paxton and John Lindley among others. They were densely packed, thoughtful, authoritative periodicals appearing weekly in some cases. The articles which appeared in their pages were written for, among others, a community of experts in their fields, by the great names of the day, recording in largely a work-a-day manner their successes and failures. Just as the nurseries themselves served as centres for scientific experiment, the periodicals served as scientific journals. The subject of horticulture was of great moment. Among other forces at work it has to be remembered that there were not the huge proliferation of shops and supermarkets such as we have today and people were not so mobile. People grew the roses they decorated their homes and gardens with and ate what their gardens produced - they could not just stop in a supermarket on their way home by car from work.

In these periodicals in an informal expansive style Thomas Rivers lays down his theories, discusses his experiments, invites the readers' participation in chasing the perfect varieties in all their intriguing forms - the more, and the more perfect, each season its own most delicious varieties. It was his aim as for his fellow experts to find fruit with exquisite flavour and texture and appearance for each day of the year; in this quest there could not be too many cultivars developed.

The Rose Amateur's Guide

As Bonks Hill House was the family home as well as the business premises for the Nursery, Thomas Rivers will have been brought up there and involved early in the family business, as with later generations. The nursery grounds extended around and beyond the house and to see how things were run and to take part was a natural and normal part of the life of the children, brought up in the expectation of taking the business on. Moreover, from boyhood, he was a great fruit eater, as he often tells us, with an interest in plants, and speaks of how he roamed the grounds, tasting and looking.

He took over the running of the nursery when his father Thomas Rivers (1770 - 1844) retired in 1827. His father may not have been in good health or may have wished to withdraw further into private life at the grander residence Landguard on Station Road in Sawbridgeworth which became his home. His son became the main occupant of Bonks Hill House and head of the business. The success achieved by the Nursery at that time is reflected in the Trades' Directories entries for Sawbridgeworth - Pigot's of 1839 lists Thomas Rivers and Son under Nursery and Seedsmen, but by 1851, Kelly lists Thomas Rivers Esquire as one of twelve gentry in the same category as the Earl Roden of Hyde Hall, and under traders, Thomas Rivers, nurseryman.

In other words when Thomas took over from his father in 1837 the business had flourished sufficiently to lift the family into the ranks of the gentry. This also meant that the business had flourished sufficiently that he could allow his gift for creative thinking to flourish and had time both to experiment and to record his visions.

In the introduction to his first book, initially published in 1837, *The Rose Amateur's Guide,* written as a 'companion to the descriptive catalogue of the Sawbridgeworth collection of roses' the firm produced, he makes reference both to the cares of running a business and his long experience even though at the time he would have just been forty years old, and goes on to indicate the extent of the grounds given to roses at the Nursery:

> As a guide...to the lovers of roses, this little treatise has been written in the few
> leisure moments allowed me by the unceasing cares of a general nursery business.
> I give the result of twenty years experience, gained by the culture of choice roses
> on a much larger scale than any where in Europe. I say this advisedly, as from
> eight to ten acres are here devoted to the cultivation of select named varieties.[3]

The rose fields
at the Nursery
Reproduced by kind permission
of Hertfordshire Archives and
Local Studies (D/Ers/ B90/ 103)

Figure 5.2

He then goes on to begin to set out his vision of the ideal, finding plants to create a succession of perfect roses for the season from summer into autumn - a quest that is echoed in the later search for fruit varieties.

> It may be asked, why, then, are so many varieties enumerated in the catalogue, if so few comparatively can be recommended? To this I reply, that some roses resemble each other in the form and colour of their flowers, yet differ much in the character of their leaves, branches and general habit. Some will also often bloom out of character, and imperfectly, one or two seasons consecutively, while others of the same colour and of the same family are blooming well…so that it is almost necessary to have plants of different natures bearing flowers alike.[4]

Here also he raises a complaint about inaccuracies in the naming of French roses, those being the source of many of the new varieties he works with to improve for English conditions, an 'inattention' to correct nomen-clature that 'has long been the bane of commercial gardening…if the original or most superior variety is ordered, ten to one if you get it'. ….This problem is one that Thomas Rivers later tackles directly in the world of British fruit growing with his call for a Pomological Society.

The book offers readers personal reflections on the nature of named varieties, their provenance and ancestry, their habit of growth, their particular features of colour or scent as well as practical advice on placing - such as to twine pillars, on groupings, aspect and cultural advice on pruning, on protection - as for example 'a thick covering of furze branches' or growing against a south wall and on fertilising.

Who are the readers? He refers to these plants as being suitable for 'every gentleman's garden' and it seems the book is couched in language and aspiration for those with extensive enough grounds in which to set numerous roses.[5] While head gardeners of grand estates and aristocrats with a personal interest in gardening would have consulted the book and yearned over the catalogue of plants to buy, it is also aimed to at the growing middle class, prosperous buyers of the time and also his fellow learned horticulturists.

The success of this book enhanced not only the reputation of the Rivers Nursery but of Thomas Rivers himself. The 1840 Rivers Catalogue lists the huge number of 200 summer roses and 250 autumn roses. 'The first were the old garden roses of the West and the second those raised from the longer-flowerers introduced from the East at the turn of the century...Rivers recalled the success of one of the most brilliant red hybrid perpetuals, Geant des Batailles: in the autumn of 1849, 8000 standards and dwarfs of this variety were dispersed over the whole face of the country..' [6]

Although Rivers' *Rose Amateur's Guide* continued to appear in new editions throughout his life - the Preface to the eleventh edition being amended in 1877, the last year of his life - by the 1840s his attention was already being drawn to the cultivation of fruit species and his observations and study focused in this direction.

The Miniature Fruit Garden or
The Culture of Pyramidal and Bush Fruit Trees

The first edition of this book appeared in 1840 as a publication separate from the Catalogue of fruit trees for sale and eventually ran to eighteen editions, the last of 1877 being prefaced by Thomas Rivers' son Thomas Francis Rivers, who had followed him into directing the fortunes of the nursery and who also made a name for himself as a developer of new varieties of fruit in particular.

Thomas Rivers directs this book to those the sixteenth edition preface terms 'numerous and increasing horticultural amateurs who seem to love to devote their leisure to the culture of fruit and fruit trees'. The success of the book has given him 'pleasure', that 'its success...is perfectly unprecedented in books devoted to horticulture'. He goes on to say that 'this little work is not designed for the gardens and gardeners of the wealthy and great, but for those who take a personal interest in fruit-tree culture, and who look on their garden as a never-failing source of amusement'. [7]

The purpose of the book is to 'advocate the culture of pyramidal fruit trees'. In other words the training of various kinds of fruit trees through branch and root pruning to grow in small spaces and to produce good quantities of crops to supply households throughout the growing season and add shapely and accessible forms to the garden. It is those who are the 'possessors of small gardens...with unfavourable soils' that his directions will most benefit.

As in his previous book, the writing is anecdotal and he gives a homely indication of how his theory of root-pruning and frequent removal of fruit trees from their planting ground came about. In 1810,

> I was a youth, [of 12], with a most active fruit-appetite, and if a tree bearing superior fruit could be discovered in my father's orchard-like nursery, I was very constant in my visits to it...In those days there was in the old nursery, first cropped with trees by my grandfather about the middle of the last century, a 'quarter' - i.e. a piece of ground devoted to the reception of refuse trees - of such trees as were too small or weak for customers; so that in taking up trees for orders during the winter they were left, and, in spring, all taken up and transplanted to the 'hospital quarter', as the labourers called it.

He describes how those trees too weak to have been chosen to be sent bare-rooted to customers in autumn and winter and sited in the hospital quarter, kept being moved, being placed closer together to save space or to tidy them up on an area of about eight acres with deep reddish loam soil where they flourished. It was among these 'refuse trees' that his boyhood cravings were satisfied with 'many a fruit-feast - such Ribston Pippins! such Golden Pippins'.

When he came to a 'thinking age' he developed a theory as to why the refuse trees bore better than the more vigorous trees and, by a friend who was a member of the Royal Horticultural Society, was encouraged to write it up for a meeting of the RHS. After much practice with the theory on the Nursery grounds, he writes *The Miniature Fruit Garden* to offer his knowledge to the general public.[8]

Rivers advocates lessons learned from Continental gardens, despite the 'prejudice against them amongst some English gardeners'. It is an indication of many visits to the Continent and evidence of his learning from his

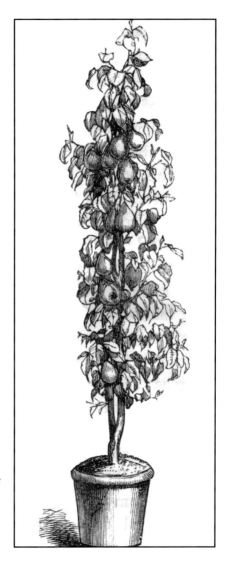

Pear tree in a pot,
figure 30 in
The Miniature
Fruit Garden

Figure 5.3

travels although no specific tales of his meetings are given here. In this book are set out his ideas about training pyramidal pears on quince root stock, and then pyramidal apples on Paradise stock as well as plum, cherry, fig, filberts in various forms.

Like the *Rose Amateur's Guide*, this book too continued to appear, published by Longman's in London, throughout the author's life, edition following edition with some amendments. He is by this time firmly established as 'a thinking man', and recognised by all fellow horticulturists as a voice to be heard. His easy style of writing must have been a reflection of his manner and personality as he made many friends in the horticultural world and welcomed visitors to what was known in the journals as the Sawbridgeworth grounds. The working atmosphere of the nursery was a good one, with long term employees happy in their work and what must have been a settled prosperous air about the business.

The Orchard House

Firmly established as a writer, Thomas Rivers was confident in offering yet another book to the public. *The Orchard House*, first published in 1850, was also very well received, again coming out in numerous editions of a thousand copies a year it appears, as did the other publications.

This book is the result of his considering how to get around the vagaries of the climate.

> It was I think about the year 1845, that the late Dr. Lindley said in a half-triumphant manner - we had had several consecutive fruitful seasons - 'Who will now say that England is not a good fruit country?' Alas for the short-lived triumph! In 1853, I find in my journal the following melancholy entry: summer cold and unfavourable; no pears, no plums, no cherries, no apples; this being the

seventh consecutive year of failure in the crop of fruit in the south of England. ...
and owing to the failure of these seasons, my attention was more closely drawn
to my pear trees in pots, which, owing to having been under glass while in bloom,
and thus escaping the spring frost, bore abundantly...[9]

He hopes in his glass houses to approximate the climate of such
temperate districts of France as Angers about three hundred km south-west
of Paris, an area he seems to know well. 'We can thus, at a little expense, in
our own dear native land, reap the benefits of a warm climate, and enjoy its
choice fruits, without suffering from its oppressive heat. ...some of my
gardening friends from that region have said, on entering it [the orchard
house] "Ah! Monsieur Rivers, voici notre climat!"'

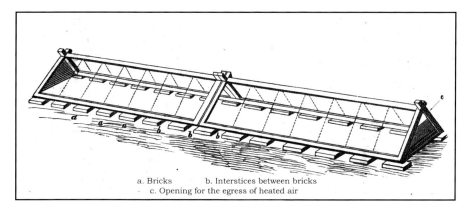

a. Bricks   b. Interstices between bricks
c. Opening for the egress of heated air

The ground vinery,
figure 22 in *The Miniature Fruit
Garden*

Figure 5.4

The success of the theory, and of the book, is made possible by the fact
that the glass constructions he advocates for the ordinary gardener had
become far less costly. Beginning with the lean-to orchard-house, he
recommends this structure to all, as '...the poor man's orchard-house; for

with a few shillings, and skill and industry, a small house may be built by the cottager, some apricots and peaches grown, and sold to his well-to-do neighbours, and his resources added to by a pleasant occupation...'

He then proceeds as with all the structures he describes in this book to give a possible dimension, then to describe its building - from the size of timbers to the dimensions of glass panes - in exact detail as well as the costs. He suggests that the structures are affordable and repay the modest expenditure. Events had conspired to cause the cost of glass to fall dramatically as in 1845 the tax on glass was abolished, this followed by the invention of plate glass. He quotes its cost, 'Sheet-glass, which when first brought into notice cost 2s. per foot, can now be bought at 2d per foot'. He also suggests that trips to Sawbridgeworth to see the structures being used in the nursery, will be helpful to poor and rich , that he needs 'not only to tell... what may be done with orchard-houses but to show what is done'. [10] He focuses not only on the timber, glass and soil substructure for the buildings but on the ventilation and heating, which produce not only the possibility of earlier fruiting without fail but improved flavour.

How did the idea of Orchard Houses come about? As always there is an anecdote. He wants to improve the culture of figs as he is very fond of them. He brings some pots of figs into the vineries and finds that the roots make their way through the bottom apertures and sink in the soil on the raised borders he uses there. 'After the crop was gathered, the pots were gently turned on one side, and the roots cut off with a knife...the plants were soon at rest with well-ripened shoots.' The next season they are top-dressed with manure and the cycle starts again, with the aim of a good crop in a warm situation and small space. He thinks why not other fruits?

'…I have now much pleasure in giving the simple method by which all these choice fruits may be grown on trees in pots, with a certainty of a crop every season…' It is the idea of the miniature fruit trees and the frequent root-pruning transferred under glass.[11]

The grand idea is to provide the setting in which the most perfect succession of perfect fruits may be achieved. He names 'for this extended mode of plum cultivation in pots' twelve varieties of dessert plum starting the cropping with Early Prolific and finishing with the Jefferson. He suggests that 'kitchen' plums might benefit from the same treatment and lists seven further varieties. He gives detailed and specific instruction about all aspects of ensuring production down to the most specific detail: 'The pots may be plunged in the soil one-third of their depth, but not more…'. [12]

This ideal, a sequence of perfect fruit to tempt every palate and meet every need, in England, in your own garden, is one that Victorian horticulturists aimed to attain. That aspiration lives on for us in the array found in supermarkets. But many of the old varieties have been lost and with them the perfection of flavour and texture that was achieved by picking at the right moment a few steps from the table where they were to be consumed.

Correspondence with Darwin

Between 1862 and 1872, Thomas Rivers and Charles Darwin, both at the height of their reputations, had a correspondence amounting to thirty-one letters now extant. Darwin had published the *Origin of Species* in 1859 but continued to research and substantiate his theories by exchanging letters with a host of people, including experts in various fields with whom he could mull over his ideas. Rivers by this time had published all three of his books and many articles but continued his work, continuing to study his practice both for the pleasure and instruction of it and developing and refining his concepts, as the prefaces to the successive editions of his books show. Darwin was very interested in botany and in using variations in plants for study. At this time he was constructing his own hothouse at Down so that he could observe tropical and tender plants. Rivers' work with glasshouses in extending the fruiting year and fostering fruit too tender for British conditions was well known.

The marvellous website for the Darwin Correspondence project summarizes all of the letters between the two and makes available the whole text of almost all. See *www.darwinproject.ac.uk*

Darwin initiates the correspondence, writing to Rivers, to ask his help with an enquiry into 'sports', that is "bud-variations" ... *interesting to anyone endeavouring to make out, what little can be made out on the obscure subject of variation.'* He acknowledges Rivers' expertise and professional standing: *'there is one little piece of information, which it is more likely that you could give me, than any man in the world, if you can spare half an hour from your professional labours & are inclined to be so kind'*. (Letter to Rivers, 3874) In a following letter Darwin speaks of having read 'with interest every scrap which you have written'. (Letter to Rivers, 3879)

In 1863, Rivers responds with equally warm courtesy to Darwin's offer of a signed copy of Origin,

> I shall be delighted to receive from you the "Origin of Species" with your name attached to it. I had it from Mudies when first published & was on the eve of ordering it from Longmans when yr. last arrived a bought copy I should of course have valued but a copy as your gift will be to me invaluab<le.> He posts him

trees, 'Pray communicate me if you have the least wish to have a tree or shrub I have so many thousands that it is always a pleasure to give—a duty to sell. (Letter to Darwin, 3933)

The correspondence becomes firmly established with Rivers venturing on some ideas that the Origin has brought to mind with Darwin responding with his own musings:

When I first read the "Origin" I was amused at what I had observed with regard to "selection". A patch of seedling trees if not transplanted seems to illustrate this (but perhaps I am taking a wrong view) the first year they are all equal in two or three years several will have pushed up—not confined to the outside of the patch which is easily accounted for by their finding more food— at the end of five or six years one or two or three will have smothered nearly all their brethren & then one alone will often be left.
(Letter to Darwin, 3965)

What you say of seedlings conquering each other well illustrates the "struggle for existence" & "natural selection". I have often & often looked at a crowd of natural seedlings with just such feelings & reflexions as yours. (Letter to Rivers, 3982)

The controversy surrounding *Origin* does not seem to worry Rivers, although he must have been regular in his attendance at his local church where his brother was a church warden and important member of the congregation. He writes to Darwin as a respected scientist whose ideas have an impact on his own observations as a horticulturist.

They begin an extended enquiry into the habits of inheritance of weeping trees. Although some of the letters of this sequence are lost, Rivers is able to provide Darwin with particulars of a weeping ash: *'You could not by any possibility have given me a more curious case of inheritance than that of the Ash, which produced weeping seedlings & itself lost the weeping peculiarity! It is capital for my purpose.'* (Letter to Rivers, 3982)

Clearly trees with a weeping variation interested Rivers, as we find in the Bonks Hill House garden to this day, a number of weeping trees such as a huge weeping beech, now under a Tree Protection Order. What remains of the garden there shows not so much a gentleman's ornamental display as the situation available for siting interesting specimen trees, as if for further study.

They also discuss their state of health, Darwin noting an absence from home to rest. Rivers responds with an interesting self-portrait, suggesting both his fitness and his appearance:

> I sincerely hope that your health is improving with age. For many long tedious years I was thin pale & delicate but on passing 55 I seemed to take a new hold of life & am now at 67 robust & vigorous. From the age of 30 to 55 I, although upwards of 6 feet in height, weighed only 10 stone I now weigh 14 & I assure you I enjoy & am very grateful for my uninterrupted good health. (Letter to Darwin, 4381)

It seems they never met. Darwin, despite Rivers' invitations, never visited the nursery although he said he wished he could have. Ill health again perhaps prevented a visit or being very occupied. They might have met at Horticultural Exhibitions though on one occasion when Rivers hopes to meet him, in 1866 when he is giving a paper to the Botanical Congress on seedling peaches, Darwin is unable to attend. The last letter in the Cambridge collection is from 1872. Thomas Rivers died in 1877 aged seventy nine, Darwin a few years later in 1882, at the age of seventy three.

This correspondence is full enough to see the qualities of fellowship in scientific enquiry, the pleasure each takes in his work, taking it beyond what is required into the realms of pure joyful speculation. Their learning feeds off the ideas of others and shares again to move further on. Their courtesy to one another is warm and personal.. As Darwin says to Rivers in Letter 3906 at the beginning of their acquaintance in 1863, 'How ignorant we are! But with the many good observers now living our children's children will be less ignorant, & that is a comfort.'

The British Pomological Society

As is clear Thomas Rivers' interests were not narrowly those of the profit of his own business but took a much wider view. In a further initiative he looked beyond Sawbridgeworth and the perfecting of growing conditions and varieties at that location and in England to consider the industry of fruit-growing in the country as a whole.

Thomas Rivers in 1873, Supplement to The Garden, August 2, 1873

Figure 5.5

In April 1854 he publishes in *The Florist, Fruitist, and Garden Miscellany* an article entitled, 'Proposal for a Pomological Society'.

> For several years it has appeared to me that we have not paid enough attention to the cultivation of fruits...How different it is with our cousins across the Atlantic! ...every state ...has its Pomological conventions...the value... of fruits discussed... In Belgium, a Royal Commission has been appointed...How cold we seem here in comparison with all this "go-a-headism!"

He goes on to suggest a society to promote discussion of the merits and demerits of new and old varieties of fruit by social exhibition meetings 'to give and obtain information: we must commence quietly, and grow vigorously.' [13]

The state of the British apple industry

The proposal in 1854 for a pomological society similar to that which existed in other countries has to be considered in the light of the fruit-growing industry of the country at the time. In the first place, there was the confusion of nomenclature that Rivers had described as a bane to the commercial grower in his first work on roses. There were as is so well described in the comprehensive study by Joan Morgan, *The Book of Apples*, a seeming proliferation of varieties of fruit, apples and other fruits too, pears and plums. '100s if not 1000s of varieties existed by the end of 18th and little was known of any - the result was that an apple was often known by a different name not only in another country or county but in an adjacent village.'[14]

One aspect of business that a careful horticulturist and nursery director had to make sure of was that the varieties his catalogue offered were all reliably named and that the qualities each possessed were carefully described and came true in the growing to the description. So while there were at the time multitudes of diverse varieties of fruit on offer as the catalogues promise, in the wider market many names were misleading, being local or simply coined by less scrupulous growers.

Also, in terms of national commerce, by 1854 sales and production of British fruit had markedly declined, even in the home market, as the orchards of Kent were not renewed and grew old and bold initiatives such as seen from the American and continental growers were not replicated in Britain. As shipping and railways had improved transport and communication links dramatically - witness the speed at which Darwin's and Rivers' letters are exchanged - distance was no longer a barrier to sales.

> At the end of the 18th c. commercial apple growing was hovering between the old world and the new. Towns and cities were growing fast together with the network of roads and canals which linked them and like every other aspect of life, the organisation of food production and distribution was changing...by the 1790's the metropolis and its affluent suburbs could buy table fruits grown as far away as Hertfordshire...
> Changes taking place in sea transport were beginning to affect British fruit growing in a different way...it became possible ...for North America, and later for the countries of the Southern Hemisphere, to send...barrels of fine apples to England... In 1838 Britain's free trade policy led to lowering of the duty on imported apples and cheap French apples undercut the Eng producers at every turn, in 1840's orcharding and fruit tree management were at their lowest ebb... a decade later the Horticultural Society itself had started to ail...imported American and Empire fruit ...reigned. [15]

It seems a scenario that is recognizable from our own times.

In 1855, an article in *The Cottage Gardener* described the 'First Extraordinary Meeting' of the British Pomological Society, held in Covent Garden on November 6th.

The objects of this meeting were to collect from all parts of the country specimens of the Fruits which are now in season; to correct their nomenclature; to

Block print for Rivers Catalogue
Reproduced by kind permission of Hertfordshire Archives and Local Studies D/Ers/ B92

Figure 5.6

compare their relative merits and qualities; to ascertain wherein and to what extent they are adapted to the soils and exposures in which they are grown; and to examine and report upon the merits of new and seedling varieties. [16]

The response was better than any had expected with twelve hundred specimens of the Fruits of Great Britain gathered which were 'produced under every variety of circumstance of soil, situation, aspect and mode of culture'. Thomas Rivers, it is reported, exhibited a collection of pears of the best quality grown in an orchard house.

So with this first meeting an important further step was taken in the effort to apply the science of pomology to aid the commercial apple industry. The renowned Joseph Paxton was the president of the Society and Dr. Robert Hogg, whose book offering his comprehensive efforts to identify fruit varieties soon would appear, was the Society secretary. After 1858 the Pomological Society was absorbed into the Horticultural Society's Fruit and Vegetable Committee. This committee continues as a force today in considering British industry issues.

Commemoration

His fellow pomologists had long respected Thomas Rivers' achievements. In 1870 it was decided to commission a memorial portrait to commemorate his services to horticulture. Such a large amount was subscribed that there was a sum over to be given to the Gardeners' Royal Benevolent Institution. It was to hang in the hall of the Royal Horticultural Society, with portraits of other notable figures such as Professor Lindley, James Veitch, Sir Joseph Banks.[17]

His reputation continued to grow after his death. Twenty years on, the horticultural journals continued to refer to his advances. In 1884, Robert Hogg dedicated the fifth edition of his authoritative fruit manual to him, with the inscription: 'Not that he requires a memorial other than that which he himself has raised; but for forty years we were knit together by the closest friendship, working together and stimulating one another in the study of pomology: and now that he has passed away I thus cherish in my memory a sincere friend and a good man.'[18]

The creation of new varieties

The modern science of genetics, based on an understanding of the laws of the transmission of hereditary characteristics that now informs the manipulation of genes in plant development, had not yet come into being. What Darwin was pondering and what Rivers was doing was part of the discovery process that would lead to such thinking. In Rivers' time new varieties were arrived at by more empirical methods. Rivers' creative thinking and close observation enabled him to succeed in propagating new varieties fit for his marketplace and to gain in the estimation of his contemporaries a reputation for his skill.

In an appendix entitled 'How did the varieties of fruits originate?', an American author writing in 1897 begins:

> There is universal curiosity to know how the various kinds of fruits have originated. It seems next to impossible to enlighten the public mind...The real cause of this dissatisfaction is the fact that people assume that there is something mysterious about the process of the origination of varieties... The fact is, that it is not the nature of domestic productions for like to produce like, but rather for similar to produce similar. That is, there are certain type or family characteristics which pass over to the offspring, but there is normally almost endless unlikenesses in the details...If the origins of varieties are traced it will be found that in the vast

majority of cases the variety was simply discovered, and that some one began to propagate it because he thought it to be good.[19]

Examining Rivers' practice as described by him and his fellow horticulturists of the time, we find that though the discovery principle applies, there is crucially creative imagination at work as well as careful experimentation. Rivers writes in an article in *The Gardeners' Chronicle* of 1871 how he came to develop the still famous Rivers early plums:

> I was attracted to some grand old Plum trees planted by my grandfather between 1770 -1780. Their name, I think, was the Early French plum...[which] once in four or five years bore good crops; in other years a mere sprinkling of fruit. By a sort of intuition it struck me that this tender but early Plum might be acclimatised by raising seedlings from it. Accordingly I sowed some stones, and raised some young trees. These were planted in a corner and nearly forgotten; I was then immersed in Rose culture. After some eight or ten or twelve years had elapsed, these trees commenced to bear fruit; I was struck by the precocity and goodness of one, and the great fertility and goodness of the other...[20]

One was named Early Favourite and the other Early Prolific and he records that the second had so increased in popularity it sold in quantities of fifteen to twenty thousand trees a year.

An article written at his death goes on to characterise Rivers' development process as having two plans: one is 'of selection from seedlings of known origin' and the other 'of direct cross breeding'. In either case Rivers had a 'pedigree book' and kept exact records - records which 'we may hope will one day see the light, as their value from a scientific point of view would be very great'. Practically speaking, his main aim was to extend the season of particular fruits, and generally to improve their fertility and quality. In the case of the thousands of uncrossed seedlings raised by him only an infinitesimal number were preserved. Rivers' taste was too critically exacting to allow what he thought an inferior variety to pass muster. Excellence only was perpetuated.

> In raising crosses Rivers has followed two distinct plans 1- the self fertilisation or in-and-breeding, and 2, cross-fetilisation. ...If the experiments were not carried out with so much care and accuracy as in the case of those of Mr. Darwin, yet their vast number and the length of time over which they extended may in large measure compensate for the defects in a scientific point of view. But it must be remembered that Rivers was quite aware of possible defects, and his keen eye and finely-tempered intelligence were excellent guides in the conduct of experiments. Nothing was left to chance, ... but the results obtained were the result of studious toil, minute observation, plodding perseverance, skilful experiment, and profound investigation. Hence his successes were no mere chapters of accident, but an onward series of philosophic sequences.[21]

Although it seems that Rivers' records have not been preserved, some of the fruit varieties that were the outcome of his thinking are still available, mainly from specialist growers. His reputation is undiminished.

Notes

1. 'Thomas Rivers', *The Gardeners' Chronicle,* Oct 27, 1877, p. 522.
2. J*ournal of Horticulture and Cottage Gardener,* August 24, 1899, p. 161.
3. Thomas Rivers, Introduction to *The Rose Amateur's Guide,* second edition (London, 1840), ix.
4. *Ibid.,* x.
5. *The Rose Amateur's Guide,* p. 104.
6. 'The first rose grower in England', *Country Life,* June 25, 1981.
7. Thomas Rivers, *The Miniature Fruit Garden or The Culture of Pyramidal and Bush Fruit Trees,* eighteenth edition (London, 1877). Preface and Introduction, vii-x.
8. *Ibid.,* x-xi.
9. Thomas Rivers, *The Orchard-House or the Cultivation of Fruit-trees under Glass,* fourteenth edition (London,1870), p. 135.
10. *Ibid.,* pp. 3, 4, 2, 34.
11. *Ibid.,* Introduction, pp. 1- 2.
12. *Ibid.,* pp. 120-121.
13. Thomas Rivers, 'Proposal for a Pomological Society', *The Florist, Fruitist, and Garden Miscellany,* April,1854, p. 108.
14. Joan Morgan and Alison Richards, *The Book of Apples* (London, 1993), p. 76.
15. *Ibid.,* pp. 103, 106.
16. 'First Extraordinary Meeting', *The Cottage Gardener,* November 14, 1855, p. 113.
17. 'The Late Mr. Rivers', *Journal of Horticulture and Cottage Gardener,* October 25, 1877, p. 328.
18. Robert Hogg, *The Fruit Manual: A Guide to the fruits and fruit trees of Great Britain* (London, 1884), Dedication.
19. R.H. Bailey, *The Principles of Fruit-Growing* (New York,1897), Appendix.
20. Thomas Rivers, *'Seedling Fruits',* The Gardeners' Chronicle, 1871.
21. *The Gardeners' Chronicle,* October 27, 1877, p. 523.

The Orchard House
in the Audley End Kitchen Garden
by Mike Thurlow

You can't help but admire the Victorians for their total industry and inventiveness. They didn't appear to harbour a negative thought in their heads.

The greatest compliment that the host of any Victorian dinner party could pay his guests was to offer them a selection of fruit and vegetables that had been grown in his own kitchen garden and were completely out of season. This allowed him to score a few valuable points in the 'one upmanship league', at the same time as impressing them with his good taste and cultured ways. Classic examples of this are the growing of pineapples, bananas, peaches and grapes at great expense in heated greenhouses. Of course whilst the host graciously received all of the compliments in his moment of glory, it was his Head Gardener who was really responsible for the success of the evening's culinary events. The head gardeners of Victorian gardens possessed a great deal of horticultural knowledge and skills that they kept stored away in their heads and notebooks. They were always looking out for new plants, equipment or growing methods that would give them an advantage over the head gardeners on other large estates. There was a great deal of professional rivalry between the head gardeners and the owners of large country gardens. It did a head gardener's employment prospects no harm to be able to stay one step ahead of the opposition.

One man who appreciated this was the great nineteenth century nurseryman, Thomas Rivers of Sawbridgeworth. He understood exactly how the minds of these head gardeners worked. He appreciated that they didn't tolerate fools and timewasters and he used this knowledge to great effect whenever he introduced new cultivars of fruit trees. They wanted trees that were reliable, produced first class fruits and also were trouble free to grow and look after. So when Mr. Rivers came up with his idea for his orchard houses in the 1840's, he went to great lengths to stress the prestige that they would bring to the owner. He had already won the head gardeners over with the promise of all sorts of fruits on demand.

Although Thomas Rivers was "the son of the Boss" he was still expected to work in the various departments of the nursery. This was to gain the valuable experience and knowledge of the company that he would need to call on when eventually he would be running the business. The notion for the orchard house came about as the result of Thomas Rivers' exceptional powers of observation and meticulous note keeping. He wanted to be able to grow figs in pots in the vineries but the trees proved to be too vigorous and grew too large. They took up more room than he could afford. So he began to search for a method of cultivation that would allow him to overcome this problem. It was common practice on the Rivers Nursery to use sunken pathways inside the greenhouses to overcome the expense of constructing wooden staging. Rivers had stood out his pot grown figs on the soil 'staging' and noticed that the roots had grown out through the drainage hole and into the soil underneath. This, he observed, allowed a harvest of good size figs to be collected from a tree grown in a relatively small sized pot. After the crop was gathered, the pots were turned over and the roots cut back to the bottom of the pot and the trees were prepared for a winter's rest. Water was withheld and the new fruiting wood was allowed to ripen in readiness for the next season. But Rivers, being the man that he was, had reasoned that the trees could develop a greater root system whilst still being grown in the same size pot if the hole at the bottom was enlarged. He had the bottoms of the pots knocked out leaving a small rim around the edge to rest large crocks on. The following spring the trees were top dressed with manure and returned to the soil beds. Thomas Rivers then asked the question if the system that he was developing worked for figs then why shouldn't it work for all the other types of fruit trees being grown on the nursery?

From this he began to developing a system of trees grown in pots under glass that he hoped would overcome the vagaries of the British climate and allow the successful cultivation of all sorts of fruits. He compared the climate inside an orchard house to that of south-west France quoting one example of being able to ripen the 'Black Hamburg' grape by the fifteenth of September in his orchard house when it wasn't ready until the twenty-fifth of the month in Angers. Rivers was always trying to keep costs down and profits up. His first attempts at developing orchard houses were little more than a wooden frames with a glass roof. They were often described as glass roofed sheds. He said that they were 'neither a vinery or a peach house or pinery'; these all belonged on the great estates and their gardens. He felt a more accurate description was for them to be called the Orchard House. Thomas Rivers had originally wanted to see his orchard houses in all of the 'small' gardens up and down the country. The truth was that their success lay in the walled kitchen gardens of the wealthy. In his book, The Orchard House, Rivers gives detailed descriptions of how to construct, manage and stock his orchard houses. He lists the lean-to orchard house, the small and large span orchard houses including examples of materials and costs. Rivers expresses a preference for the span houses because they look more agreeable and allow easier care of the trees. But he qualifies this statement by advising that the span houses are only really suitable in warm and sheltered gardens. I think that it is safe to assume that this is how the Orchard House at Audley End came to be built in 1856.

The Orchard House completed the range of glasshouses in the Kitchen Garden at Audley End House. There was the Vinery built on the south facing wall that included the early and late vines and peach houses with the Display House at the centre. There was also the Stove House and Greenhouse in which specialised crops were grown. When English Heritage began to the restoration of the Kitchen Garden during the 1980's, only the Vinery survived. It was agreed by everyone involved in the restoration of the kitchen garden that we wanted to acknowledge the existence of the Orchard House at Audley End, but how best to represent it was the problem. The simple truth was there was very little to work with apart from some iron posts and outline of the walls at soil level. In the end it was decided to cover the ground inside the walls with gravel and fix heavy timber to the top of the posts to at least give some idea of the original height of the building. To demonstrate the growing of fruit trees in pots we would grow a range of apples, pears and plums in very large pots. It wouldn't be very inspiring but at the time none of us had enough experience and knowledge to contribute more.

One of the most satisfying aspects of garden restoration is the research for historic plants and their modern day suppliers. I had already raided the catalogues of Brogdale, Scott's of Merriot and Keeper's. All of these nurseries had bent over backwards to help us in our efforts. But there we still a few gaps our fruit tree lists that required filling and I turned to Read's Nursery for help. Like all of the nurseries mentioned, Read's catalogue is stuffed full of information that makes you want to grow every single plant described on the pages. One name that noticed that kept on cropping up was that of Rivers of Sawbridgeworth.. Resistance was useless; I just had to order a representative of every fruit tree that Rivers had introduced to grow in the kitchen garden. Not long after I had placed the order I received a telephone call from Mrs. Read asking if it would be possible to deliver the trees in person and perhaps have a look around the garden. I was only too pleased to say, 'Yes, of course you can'. The day for the delivery arrived and we weren't to be disappointed with the quality of the trees. The excitement of reading off the names of these wonderful old varieties inside the red brick walls of a kitchen garden is a special feeling. It is almost as if you are bringing them home. Mr. and Mrs. Read were full of enthusiasm and explained that they were also in the process of restoring their walled garden. As we walked around the garden we eventually came to the remains of the orchard house. Terence Read immediately identified it as a Rivers orchard house and asked what was happening on the site. Rather embarrassedly I explained our intentions. He was just as disappointed as we had been.

A couple of weeks after this visit I received a package from Terence Read. It was a photocopy of the 1858 edition of Rivers' The Orchard House with the simple message, 'I thought that this may be of a little help to you'. It was the first time that I had ever seen anything like it. It was full of descriptions and lists of trees and pages on how to manage an orchard house. When I first began to study the document I wasn't prepared for what the words '...a little help'. meant. There was the story of the development of the orchard house, the various types of orchard houses and a description of the orchard house recently built for the Lord Brayebrooke at Audley End. There it was before me. A full description and diagrams of the orchard house that Rivers had designed and built at Audley End. He gives all of the measurements for the walls and sashes (windows). The dimensions of twenty feet in width and ninety feet in length fitted perfectly with the footprint of the building. The height is given as ten feet with the roof being 'supported by a row of two inch iron pillars along the centre about seven feet apart'. These of course were the iron posts referred to earlier that had survived the demolition of the original orchard house. I passed this information on to Nick Hill, the English Heritage project manager, and I think that it is true to say that from that moment onwards Nick was determined to reconstruct the Audley End Orchard House.

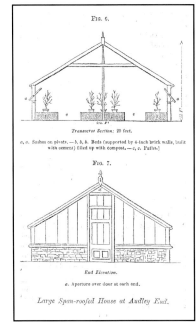

Fig. 6.
Transverse Section: 20 feet.
a, a. Sashes on pivots. — b, b, b. Beds (supported by 4-inch brick walls, built with cement) filled up with compost. — c, c. Paths.
Fig. 7.
End Elevation.
a. Aperture over door at each end.
Large Span-roofed House at Audley End.

Orchard House at Audley End from Thomas Rivers, *The Orchard House*, sixth edition, c 1858. Figure T.1

The first stages of the restoration of the kitchen garden were nearing completion and one day Nick Hill came to see me and said, 'If it was possible to rebuild the orchard house how would you manage it?'

I replied that of course we would be honour bound to use the system that Rivers had written about. This meant using fruit trees worked on vigorous rootstock ands growing them in pots with no bottoms in them. At the same time I hadn't the faintest idea of what we could be letting ourselves in for.

The Audley End restoration foundation
Before (insert)
After (main)
Reproduced by kind permission of M. Thurlow
Figure T.1 & T2

'Fine'. He said, 'I can tell you that we are going to go ahead and put it back!'

I couldn't believe what I was hearing. After all of the wishing and hoping it was finally going to happen. There was a long period of measuring and re–measuring the site. Eventually a set of working drawings were produced in accordance with Mr. Rivers' instructions. All of the timber frame work was to be pre- fabricated off site. During the early winter of 2000 work began on building the low brick walls. The excitement of seeing the building rising up once more is still with me to this day. English Heritage wanted to remain faithful to the original construction methods and lime mortar was used to bind the bricks. The problem with lime mortar is that it isn't frost proof until it has hardened over several months. During the Christmas period we experienced several nights of really hard frosts and the mortar failed. When the building team returned to work in the new year they were faced with crumbling walls that had to be rebuilt. It was a disappointing set back but work moved on.

By the spring of 2001 the timber frame work started to arrive on site and at last you could sense the scale and beauty of the building. A 'really noble as well as a nobleman's orchard house, and forms a healthy and most agreeable promenade', writes Thomas Rivers. There were a few problems getting the construction right and this delayed the handover of the building by a few months. The trees had already been ordered and were potted up and stood out under the vines awaiting their brand new home. At last the great day arrived and we were able to take possession of the Orchard House. The first job that we had to do was to fill up the raised beds. The bottom half was filled with brick rubble and there was plenty of that lying around! The top half was topped up with ordinary garden soil. To settle the soil as much as possible it had to be flooded with water and allowed to drain through. A few days later we were able to set out the fruit trees in their final quarters. Out of necessity we have had to use pot grown and field grown trees. The field grown trees always struggle to survive after being squeezed into a 12"/30cm pot. We have suffered most of our losses when using the field grown trees. Fruit trees resent having their roots cut back too much and Rivers acknowledges this by advising only to use pot grown trees or growing the trees on in pots first before transferring them into larger pots

After the initial euphoria of having the Orchard House up and running had settled, we began to experience the first of many problems when growing fruit trees in pots. The really big headache was finding a suitable potting compost. Traditionally, a loam based John Innes No 3 type of compost would have been used. Because of our organic status we are unable to use this compost so we began to experiment in trying to make up our own potting compost. After a couple of false starts, we decided to use garden soil with added grit for drainage. This has proved to be successful. One word of warning - avoid using soil containing too much clay as it impedes free drainage even when the grit is used. All the members of the stone fruit family must have perfect drainage. We also started losing trees after the winter resting period. At first I thought that perhaps they had suffered from frost damage because there is no heat in the orchard house. The losses were spread across all types of trees and there didn't seem to be a common factor. We had followed Rivers' advice but still the trees were struggling to survive. After searching everywhere for any scrap of information that might give us any sort of clue as to where we were going wrong I read an article that suggested that the trees shouldn't repotted during the spring as Rivers had recommended in his earlier publications. In later editions, Rivers revises this piece of advice and promotes that any repotting or top dressing is carried during the autumn. The chances of success are enhanced if the trees are pinched pruned during the second half of the summer and are liquid fed weekly until October before being then rested for the winter.

We have discovered that the trees are put under great stress when grown in the 12"/30cm to 18"/45cm pots. This puts too much strain upon the root system of the tree. Fruit trees produce masses of vegetative growth and need water and nutrients to support it. We used to be visited by a lovely old gent from Sussex whose family used to manage fruit trees under glass. He was the last of the line and had read about our orchard house and was intrigued at the thought of growing fruit trees in pots. He told me that they used to grow their trees directly in the soil and that the critical period was the summer flush of growth that produced the next seasons fruit bearing wood. 'We had to top apply a top dressing of nitrogen and give them as much water as they wanted to encourage the growth,' he said.

This statement is supported by an entry of William Cresswell who was a journeyman gardener at Audley End during the summer of 1874. For the entry dated 2nd of July 1874 he writes that "The fruit trees in the orchard house were stood up on bricks to allow water to pass off freely". This entry suggests that the system of allowing the roots to grow into the soil beds had already been abandoned during the intervening eighteen years. Perhaps like us they had found that the soil directly underneath the pots became boggy due to the large amounts of watering that is required to sustain the plants. This in turn affected the free drainage of the pots creating waterlogged conditions around the roots. Another consideration when trying to use the smallest pot possible is of course pot-bound trees that aren't able to benefit from the extra watering and feeding. Rivers insists that the pot should be large enough for only one man being needed to lift it. Gradually though we were beginning to develop the idea that we would have to use larger pots. The evidence to support this theory came from an unexpected source.

I had been invited to visit the Rivers Nursery by John Sapsford. His father had been a fruit foreman at the nurseries and John showed me several photographs of Rivers' own orchard houses. The first thought that struck me was that the trees were being grown in very large pots and that the pots were standing on the soil floor of the house. What had happened to the notion of growing the trees in small pots on raised beds? And this was in Rivers' own orchard house at Sawbridgeworth in the early part of the twentieth century. The photograph also reminded us that when we first looked at the orchard house base back in 1999 you could see the remains of the bases that were built to support the heating system that had been installed at a later date. There was evidence perhaps to prove that the raised beds at Audley End had also been removed at some time. This was so uncanny because by growing the fruit trees in pots stood upon the raised beds you were actually losing potential fruiting area just to accommodate the height of the wall. Just as important for pest control, the tops of the trees are growing in the hot dry air at the top of the orchard house. This of course is fertile country for red spider mite. The only real control against RSM is damping down but it is very difficult to maintain because the ridge area is always the first to dry out.

The restoration of the Rivers Orchard House at Audley End has been a rewarding experience because we have gone through all of the trials and tribulations of our predecessors and somehow managed to arrive at a similar conclusion to them. This is the one of the great benefits of restoration projects. They force you to explore and experience the past at first hand. Rivers' original orchard house survived in to the 1960's when it became unsafe and had to be demolished. Originally we stocked with a wide selection of fruit trees that he recommended and of course was able to supply from his own nursery. Since 2000 we have discovered from old planting lists that the Orchard House was mainly used to grow peaches and nectarines. Growing these trees under cover prevents peach leaf curl that they would suffer from if grown outside without any form of protection from the winter rains. We are in the course of assembling a collection of Rivers introductions to complement and celebrate his noble structure.

Mike Thurlow is the Head Gardener of the Organic Kitchen Garden at Audley End in Saffron Walden, a stately home owned by English Heritage.

Chapter Six
The Rivers Nursery
and Family in Local Society

As might be expected, the Rivers family played an important part in the life of the community. As their status as important landowner and employer followed their success in business, their parish duties increased and more of their activities were noted in publications that have survived. It was not the case that all family members stayed in Sawbridgeworth - many of those not involved in the Nursery went elsewhere to seek their fortunes, some abroad, to South Africa for example, to Canada too. Others chose to make a career elsewhere in England in other fields. Those who stayed in Sawbridgeworth were not necessarily involved with the family nursery business. Women married into other families or if single, are at times heard of as living in houses on Rivers land.

The Rivers family and Great St Mary's Church

Church and church activities played an important role in the life of all residents in the eighteenth and nineteenth centuries. In the parish of Sawbridgeworth, the church of Great St. Mary was the Rivers family church. The first documentary reference to this church is from the Domesday Book though there is evidence on the site of building from the eleventh century. It is constructed of flintstone and mortar in the style of Hertfordshire churches where there is no local source of grand building stone, and has a square battlemented tower with a characteristic Hertfordshire spike. From the eighteenth century the parish registers carry the names of various members of the Rivers family as do the gravestones in the Churchyard though many stones in the Rivers family areas are frost-bitten and moss-covered, too damaged to read. There are some large old trees, fine specimens of their species, in the burial ground surrounding the church building. These include some of those known to be grown and distributed by Rivers Nursery, such as an enormous Wellingtonia, *(Sequoiadendron giganteum,)* near the main church entrance.

Gravestone
commemorating Mary,
second wife of Thomas
Rivers of Bonks Hill,
in the Gt. St. Mary's Churchyard
Reproduced by kind permission
of Gt. St. Mary's Church

Figure 6.1

Those who were outstanding in the community played their part in officiating in the affairs of the Church. Therefore, we see a number of names connected with the Nursery in the records of the Church. One in particular stands out and for him there is a fairly good account of the role he played. This was Henry R. Rivers, likely to have been a younger brother of the third Thomas Rivers. Henry Rivers may or may not have been involved running the Nursery business - there is no clear evidence of that surviving - but he was a Church Warden at Gt. St. Mary's, a very important role for a local notable for the Church and for the community it served. Henry Rivers played a key role in one of the traditional duties of Church Wardens, ensuring the upkeep of the fabric of the building. That he kept a diary, maybe a Church Warden's diary, is known from quotations taken from it that appear in the *Story of Sawbridgeworth*. The diary itself has not been discovered, either in the HALS collection or in Parish documents. Quoted from his diary is the stark statement: 'Until the year 1845 the church had been allowed to fall into a most deplorable state of dilapidation...the nave roof let in the water, the windows were mostly decayed...the church furniture was in the most neglected condition...' In 1849, the Curate, a Mr. Coker, and Mr. Rivers started a subscription. Following their call and the substantial funds raised, the nave was rebuilt from the arches and a new roof was raised.[1]

Thomas Rivers, who had just published in 1850 one of his three successful books on new ideas in horticulture, *The Orchard House*, donated the proceeds of the first edition to this church repair fund. Henry Rivers' efforts in driving the building effort and its funding are commemorated for all time - his carved head became a stop of one of newly fixed arches.[2]

A newspaper clipping, extant in the *Newspaper Cuttings Book of 1878 - 1901* kept by Henry R Rivers, records the reopening of Great St. Mary's in 1872 with a 'vast improvement effected' only marred by the 'melancholy circumstance' of the sudden death of the foreman of the works one morning

Image of Henry Rivers, nave arch stop

Reproduced by kind permission of Gt. St. Mary's Church

Figure 6.2

as he was leaving for his employment. It was also noted that despite the huge sum raised for the work, the funds did not stretch to laying on gas to the Church.[3] Rivers' signature is found on Parish registers as an overseer of the distribution of the Tithes. Church Wardens were effectively treasurers of the church, and the distribution of the tithe - the most important church revenue, based on a tenth of all produce both land and labour - was still a vital matter for church and community. By the nineteenth century the tithe had been commuted to money payments rather than payments in kind.

Rivers Nursery and its employees' welfare

Later in his life, when his brother Thomas' son, Frank Rivers, was the director of the Nursery, Henry Rivers also provides direct insight into another of the Rivers' company civic duties, care of their employees. In his Newspaper Cuttings Book he places an article about the anniversary dinner and entertainment in 1883 of the 'sick fund' society. The sick fund is described: all workmen are eligible and most in the firm subscribe, the older hands paying 2d a week and the boys half of that and the company directors contributing what the article calls a generous five guineas a year to enable staff to have up to eight weeks full pay, eight weeks half, amounting to sixteen weeks in all. It is a scheme based on 'self-help and thrift'. William Camp, one of the notable general managers, is the Chairman of the fund.

The anniversary dinner is the annual dinner celebrating the occasion and offering the Nursery a chance to host the employees and their families. It is held in one of the huge forcing glasshouses, one hundred and fifty feet long, cleared for the occasion. The dinner features an enormous joint of beef weighing sixty-six pounds. There are toasts to the Queen and royal family, to Henry Rivers and T.F. Rivers who appear only for the enter - tainment after the dinner with their families. The firm is complimented for the kind and liberal way it treats its employees and by this time the cheers are raising the roof. Music follows with various company employees on a stage playing, with William Camp on the violin.[4]

Other company occasions were arranged, including the summer trip for employees' families in a charabanc to the seaside remembered by Tup stubbings Armes.[5] It was not just in articles that the company was remembered as a benevolent employer. In the memories of employees it was considered a good workplace, one in which the employees' welfare, by the standards of the time, was taken into account and good provision for housing and other benefits made.

Henry Rivers' cuttings book focuses also on local society events, church events in his own and other parishes and events such as the marriage in 1861 of his nephew, Frank Rivers, who took over the running of the Nursery as his father became older, around 1870. His was a 'fashionable wedding at

Coalpit Heath, Westerleigh' near Bristol to the daughter of a coal works owner, an occasion of 'rejoicing peculiar to rustic festivities' by the gentleman's 'humble cottagers from around his estate'.[6]

Local horticulture shows

Rivers Nursery, while winning gold medals in the great national horticultural shows, also set up displays in the local shows. Margaret Rivers, daughter of the last Thomas Rivers, is remembered by local people as a girl on stage at the shows handing out prizes for various competition entries.

A Rivers display
in Memorial Hall Sawbridgeworth
in the 1950s.
Reproduced by kind permission
of John Sapsford

Figure 6.3

The weeping ash and
purple beech,
central features on the green
outside the local surgery.
Photograph Elizabeth Waugh

Figure 6.4

Specimen trees in Sawbridgeworth

A reminder of the Nursery in Sawbridgeworth that brings continuous
pleasure to all local inhabitants, whether aware or unaware of the Rivers
heritage, is the presence of outstanding trees of species that Rivers
particularly promoted. One is the purple beech, Fagus sylvatica riversii, a
Rivers variety, noted by Alan Mitchell as 'a superior dark red form' and
excused from his general condemnation of other copper beeches as heavy in
colour and disfiguring of the general landscape.[7] Others include weeping ash
and weeping beech.

Rivers family houses and gardens

The agricultural land needed for developing a horticulture business came with an assortment of farm and village buildings, so that from the early days acquiring land for the Rivers business, whether through renting or buying, also meant acquiring both working areas and housing. These farmhouses became homes not only for the Rivers family but for some of the nursery workforce too. Certain houses were commonly allocated to people in certain positions in the Nursery; for example Weeping Ash bungalow situated beside Bonks Hill House was usually the general manager's house. Some employees and their families lived in tied houses as was agricultural practice and when they left their jobs, they generally had to leave their houses too. The Rivers family lived in these nursery properties too, and in time houses accommodated family members who rented from the business but were not directly involved in it, including maiden aunts and brothers working in other employment. Looking at a number of these Rivers properties in detail traces the growth and decline of the business and the social status of property dwellers as well as the changes in the population and prosperity of the area as measured against the continuity of ownership of Rivers Nursery.

Housing for the family: Bonks Hill House

The most important house and the one which reflects the nursery fortunes most closely is Bonks Hill House. It was acquired as the major residence, but more significantly as the shop front or trading place in the early days when John Rivers set up a business in 1725. Bonks Hill was at that time a farmhouse of seventeenth century origin according to the Listed Buildings Register, opening directly onto the main London - Cambridge road.[8] Behind it spread the fields where horticultural cultivation of various kinds could take place and where eventually extensive glasshouses were built. At first the house and growing area were probably no more than twenty acres, though it is likely that more land was leased. A surviving sales agreement of 1789 shows land being purchased as the business prospered, the Rivers holdings growing eventually through various transactions to more than three hundred acres in the nineteenth century, much of it spreading westward along the High Wych road from Bonks Hill to High Wych village. Like the business, this house stayed in the family from the earliest period through to the closing down of the nursery.

Bonks Hill House about 1970.

Reproduced from *Nurseryman and Garden Centre*, 1975

Figure 6.5

The early business was characterised by its meeting customers' needs in a variety of ways. The social nature of the transactions was emphasized by a swinging sign on the house, 'The Fox', as recorded in the Journal of Horticulture and Cottage Gardener. In the early days not only did the business sell 'fruit trees and forest trees to the neighbouring gentry, cabbage plants for those who had gardens and market-garden produce for those who had none; flowers, fruit, and nosegays ...and, that the tastes of each might be further gratified, one of the staple commodities was a glass of good currant wine ...from a cellar dated 1761 on an inscribed stone'. The article continues that the business had by then become so successful that a Rivers had become 'the proprietor of the place he and his father had previously occupied as tenants'.[9]

Though the original timber building continued in use as it does even now, in the early nineteenth century a number of changes occurred. In the first place, through discussion with the two major landholders on either side of the main road, the Rivers Nursery and the Pishiobury Estate, a Turnpike Trust formed of local prominent citizens carried out a major engineering project on the road. It had long been a subject of debate as the hill at that point was very steep and caused particularly in times of bad weather slow or impossible going. The sharp incline was somewhat leveled, taking the earth from the heights and putting it in the lower reaches where there had been a ford at the brook crossing, and straightening the road so that it led more directly south. A faster more efficient road service was in this way achieved, better for all as the road was, and remains, a major thoroughfare and route for businesses back and forth between the urban areas it crosses.[10]

However, after the road project was complete the Bonks Hill site no longer connected directly to the main road. The nursery entrance was then shifted around the corner to the High Wych road where it remained.

Therefore as the business had continued during previous period to develop and expand, acquiring more land stretching towards the High Wych village now through purchase rather than lease, the office for business moved to Wiseman's farm area where it remained through various transformations until the business was sold in the late 1980s.

Although the nursery workers still walked through to the working areas and glasshouses via paths through Bonks Hill grounds, it must have changed from being both residence and working area to being residence only. As the fortunes of the company were reaching their highest point in the nineteenth century, the original wooden farmhouse was partly taken down and a more elegant Georgian extension built as it became a gentleman's dwelling. All this can clearly be seen in the architecture of house now.

This was the time of the great pomologist Thomas Rivers (1798 - 1877) who through his own writing and that of visitors as recorded in the horticultural journals of the day, gives us a view of his life at the nursery. Though the house after being extended was more strictly residential, it retained its direct connection with the business and Thomas Rivers used what seem to be daily walks through the grounds, sampling the fruit, to make observations on the growth of the plants and to consider modifications in methods of nurturing stock and propagating new strains. He welcomed visitors.

The nineteenth century was for the Rivers business and for the customers in Britain and in the Empire that it served, a time of prosperity and stability. The nursery way of life this third Thomas describes is likely to have continued in much the same way through the time of Thomas Francis Rivers who succeeded his father in directing the nursery and who went on to develop the Conference pear and to receive the RHS Veitch Medal for services to horticulture.

Changes were brought about by the changing times as well as by changes in the directors. When Bonks Hill house stood empty at the death of Henry S. Rivers, and WWII began, the military commandeered the house about 1939. During this period it received somewhat rough usage and though the family received a grant for repairs when it was restored to them in 1946, there had been damage to floor boards, tiles, glass and the walls had been strung with communication wires. The last Thomas Rivers and his family lived there until after his death in 1978. Bonks Hill House was sold in 1981.[11]

Bonks Hill House garden

What remains today of the landscaping of the garden area surrounding the house is notable mainly for surviving specimen trees. While in the early days it must have been farm yard and business area, no doubt during the nineteenth century care was taken to lay it out with enclosed areas for family use and a lawn, much of it hard to decipher as periods of neglect have taken their toll. During WWII, the extensive front lawn was parking for military vehicles and the area around one of the huge old wellingtonias was where used oil was poured, to the detriment of the tree's well being. One such wellingtonia was recently found to be unsafe by the present owner and with the agreement of the tree protection officer, was taken down. The area is in a designated conservation zone so protection is offered to the collection that remains. It seems that a number are part of a group of weeping trees - planted in the nursery manner, their habit of growth to be observed and discussed by the third Thomas with Darwin. Though these trees are set in the house grounds they seem not so much to enhance it as a grand dwelling or to create an atmosphere as to exist as exemplars of their species. [12]

Landguard, Station Road

Landguard 2009
Photograph Elizabeth Waugh
Figure 6.6

The listed buildings register describes Landguard as an eighteenth century dwelling 'remodelled as a Regency cottage ornee' in the early nineteenth century with a lean-to vine house or conservatory. The house is listed as Hamptons on the OS map of 1879 but it is thought the name was changed to Landguard after a fort in Suffolk by an owner with military connections at the end of the nineteen century, perhaps with reference to its position at the top of a hill off Station road. The Sawbridgeworth Manor Court Book (ref.

28139 in Hertfordshire Archives and Local Studies) contains a sales document seems to indicate that Thomas Rivers Senior (1770 -1844) purchased between 1806 and 1808 part of a holding owned by Robert Hampton, gardener. A cottage ornee is described as a villa on a small scale, which may be characterised by a garden-front opening into a picturesque lawn varied by groups of trees. This description certainly fits Landguard, a pleasant gentleman's home, not the home of a business like Bonks Hill.

It seems that the purchase of this house is another indication of the family's rising position in society in the early nineteenth century. It is a Rivers home in Sawbridgeworth but at a distance from the nursery grounds and came into use for Thomas Rivers the elder when Bonks Hill became the house of the third Thomas in 1827 when the business passed from father to son. That is, it seems when the father was no longer closely working in the business he was able to withdraw to another part of town, leaving the care of the business to his son.[13]

Housing for workers: Gilders

The old farmhouse that was the dwelling for the Gilders Farm, was acquired by Rivers as more and more acres became part of the business. It is likely that it too was a seventeenth century farmhouse like the original Bonks Hill House. Of timber-frame and plaster construction, it was located on Brook Lane, one of the paths that led up from the main road to the nursery grounds and on to High Wych village, cutting through the meadows stretching out around the house where corn and strawberries were grown.

The Sapsford family lived in this house after Arthur Sapsford came back from his period in France to take up employment at Rivers again and John, his son, was born there in 1922. The family did not stay in this house very long, Arthur's wife choosing to move up to High Wych for the sense of community rather than living in this rather isolated farmhouse.

Joan Powell, who lived in Gilders with her family from her birth in 1929 for ten years, while her father Ernest Traveller was employed by Rivers, remembers the house as large and rambling with space enough for a family with many children and a high brick wall. Though it was on a country lane with only one or two other houses nearby, she had her brothers and sisters as playmates and there was the brook to paddle in and the fields to wander

Gilders farmhouse c. 1920
Reproduced by kind permission of John Sapsford

Figure 6.7

through. She remembers it as a time of freedom before leaving school at age fourteen for a harder adult life. When her father left Rivers to begin war work in 1939, the family had to leave this home.

The garden at Gilders was productive, with a big orchard perhaps pre-dating the Rivers period. As in the Nursery during the times when the Rivers business sold market garden produce or displayed high quality fruit at horticultural shows, fruit was stored on shelves in farm buildings, carefully racked to protect and prolong the eating quality so as to have fruit throughout the year. Water cress was grown in the brook. There was a nanny goat remembered very well by Joan's playmates as having to be pacified by offering grass, and as in other country houses of the time, the family kept rabbits for eating.[14]

Later when the pressure of population growth in the 1960s came, the old farmhouse was pulled down to make way for new housing estates on what had been Rivers land, along Burnside and the Crest, where once a bank of flowers marked the edge of Rivers Nursery. A large chestnut tree on the High Wych footpath from Brook Lane marks the spot where the farmhouse once stood.

Wisemans Cottages, No 54 and 56 High Wych Road

The listed buildings register describes these cottages as a single cottage of seventeenth century origin, later divided. It is a tall timber frame and plaster structure with a red tile roof. It was on land that must have been acquired as nursery grounds in the early times. According to the present owner's research the area in which the cottage is located came to be called Manfield Common and was within a field largely unchanged from Domesday on. The

Wisemans Cottages.

Photograph Elizabeth Waugh

Figure 6.8

property coming early into the Rivers landholdings remained as rented housing throughout the nursery business period.[15] One part finally became the home of Eileen Tybjerb who worked in the office during the final years in the 1980s, sold in 1985 as part of the estate. It is typical of the numerous houses lining the High Wych Road that were Rivers' houses and rented to employees. It was desirable for both the employer and the employees that the staff worked close by, mostly within the range of the sound of Rivers' big bell that rang every morning to call people to work.

The Rivers bell near the
Office in Wisemans that
rang the employees to
work over the years
Reproduced by kind permission
of John Sapsford

Figure 6.9

Like the many village houses that embody some of the Rivers Nursery history, so too the street names. New houses now stand on former Rivers Nursery land, some in roads named Nursery Fields. An entire area is named The Orchards, which though surely planted up at some time with Rivers Nursery trees, may commemorate orchards that predated the Rivers period.

Notes

1. Sawbridgeworth W.E.A., *The Story of Sawbridgeworth, Book 2 The Churches and the People,* edited by Lionel Munby, (1966), p. 42.
2. *The Parish Church of Great St. Mary, Sawbridgeworth* (Church Guide, 2009), p. 25.
3. 'Reopening of Sawbridgeworth Church', *Herts and Essex Observer,* Oct. 2, 1872 in *Newspaper Cuttings Book* compiled by Henry R. Rivers of Sawbridgeworth, 1878 - 1901. Hertfordshire Archives and Local Studies, Acc 3607.
4. 'Anniversary Dinner and Entertainment at Messrs. T. Rivers and Son's Nursery', *The Herts and Essex Observer,* Jan. 6, 1883 in *Newspaper Cuttings Book.*
5. Tup Armes, Recorded Interview, 18 March 2009.
6. 'Fashionable Wedding at Coalpit Heath, Westleigh', *The Bristol Daily Post,* Friday,

August 23, 1861 in *Newspaper Cuttings Book.*
7.	Alan Mitchell, *A Field Guide to the Trees of Britain and Northern Europe* (London, 1974), p.221.
8.	Department of the Environment, List of Buildings of Special Architectural or Historic Interest, Sawbridgeworth.
9.	*Journal of Horticulture and Cottage Gardener,* October 25, 1877.
10.	*The Story of Sawbridgeworth,* Book 1, pp.28-29.
11.	Nigel Rivers, Recorded Interview, April 5, 2009.
12.	*Ibid.* Margaret Rivers, Recorded Interview, March 30, 2009.
13.	*Journal of Horticulture and Cottage Gardener,* October 25, 1877.
14.	Recorded Interview, Joan Powell, 26 February 2009. John Sapsford.
15.	Research material from Robert Smith.

Chapter Seven
Into the Twentieth Century

Another notable horticulturist

Thomas Francis Rivers (1831-1899), known as Frank, had come into the business working beside his father, the great third Thomas. He had taken over direction of the nursery five years at least before his father's death in 1877 and he had been doing his own experiments in developing new fruit varieties earlier. During the course of his life, his own achievements were certainly recognised by the horticultural world as he gathered its honours. He was an early recipient of the Veitch Memorial Medal, named for his father's fellow nurseryman, James Veitch of Chelsea, recognising work in developing new and improved varieties. In 1897 he was awarded the highest honour given by the Royal Horticultural Society, the Victoria Medal of Honour. His was one of the first sixty medals to be given in the first year of the Award's existence. His funeral in Sawbridgeworth was attended not only by his family and local society but by horticulturists, including Robert Hogg, distinguished colleague and friend of his father, and others representing the authoritative and prestigious gardening journals of the day.

It is recorded in his obituaries published in these journals that his aims in his work were to extend the fruit season, 'either by securing early varieties, or by lengthening the period by evolution of late varieties'. [1] While unlike his father Frank Rivers did not write prolifically so that there is no full record of his thinking, certainly the catalogue of fruit-trees and roses issued for 1897 by the Rivers Nursery, surviving in the Lindley Library and in the Hertfordshire Archives, is a good summary of what Frank Rivers was striving for.

T. Francis Rivers
Reproduced by kind permission
of Hertfordshire Archives and
Local Studies (D/ERs/B90/ file 2)

Figure 7.1

The range of this catalogue in terms of the breadth of seasons covered and in depth of numbers of varieties to satisfy and stimulate demand for a range of flavour, texture and appearance is astonishing to the modern fruit eater. The catalogue is selling what no supermarket of modern times reaching out for its supplies around the world could possibly match. In addition, the trees were offered in a number of forms: for a dwarf fruit orchard, as standards, for pyramids, for growing in pots in orchard houses, trained into cordons, double cordons, bushes, as espaliers or edging for borders.

Apples and pears, plums and more

For example, from Rivers Nursery in 1897 we might have purchased for a Dwarf Fruit-Tree Orchard: twenty-one varieties of Culinary Apples, ripening from August to March; fifteen varieties of Dessert Apples, ripening from August to March on Nonesuch and broad-leaved Paradise rootstock; and twenty varieties of Culinary Apples raised on crab rootstock.

This tempting bounty for dwarfing in a confined area is in addition to the offer of about one hundred and thirty varieties of apples as standard orchard trees or for other kinds of training. We might have bought any of one hundred varieties of pears, or any of seventy kinds of plums, not to mention our choice of apricots, cherries, currants, figs, gooseberries, grapes, medlars, nectarines, peaches, nuts, oranges, lemons, limes. Moreover, the Rivers interest in roses continued with over two hundred listed, including one named 'Charles Darwin'.

The catalogue also notes that Gold Medals had been awarded to the Rivers collections at the RHS Agricultural Hall, the Crystal Palace, the Temple Gardens, the Earl's Court Exhibition, the Liverpool Exhibition, Manchester Botanic Gardens.

The *Gardeners' Chronicle* obituary has a shorter list, naming a few of the principal plants Frank Rivers himself developed. These include the Conference pear as well as the Thomas Rivers apple, the Early Rivers nectarine, the late Transparent plum among a select list of about thirty varieties of different fruits. In other words, his accomplishment was great and reflects the aim of the Victorian gardener that his father too had reached for - to have a plethora of delicious fruit available for the longest possible annual period. Their imagination and skills in growing enabled this kind of choice to be made reality.

It is also clear that many of their buyers would be able to support the expense of setting up an extensive fruit area supported by glasshouse culture. However, the dwarfing stock choice shows the effort to create an extensive assemblage of fruit cultivars for those smaller buyers with less land. Unfortunately there are no surviving order books from this period to give us names of customers.

Of all the fruit on the list, the Conference pear, satisfying both our appetites and the distributors' need for durability, continues to reach a mass market today; we, though less discriminating than the Victorians, obviously enjoy this pear in bulk.

Oranges around the world

The vast stock list reflects not only vast sales in Britain, but sales to the far-flung areas of the world. Citrus fruit seems to have been in particular demand abroad. In 1876, Valencia Late, one of a number of varieties of orange sent to California from Rivers proved better suited to West coast conditions than Florida varieties and can be credited with starting the California orange industry.[2] Letters survive in Kew from Frank Rivers detailing

Detail of the Ordnance
Survey map sheet
XXX1, 6 inches to the
mile, 1878, showing
some of Rivers holdings
marked with trees,
labelled Nursery.
Reproduced by kind permission
of Hertfordshire Archives and
Local Studies

Figure 7.2

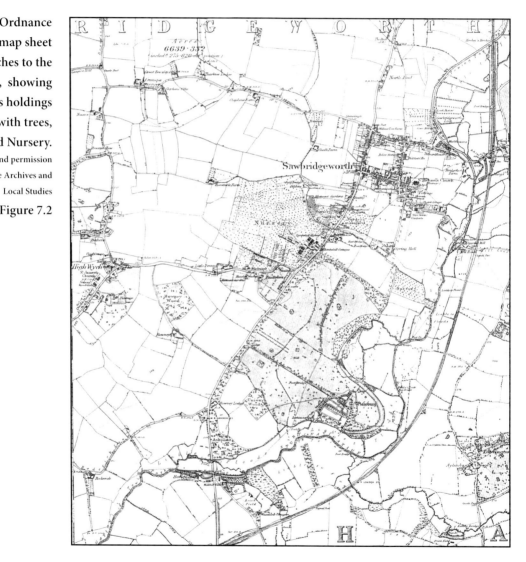

orders filled: among them, Mr. Dyer of Kew has ordered orange trees to be sent to the Horticultural Gardens, Lucknow, India in 1887. Other orders were filled for South Africa.[3]

Rivers Nursery was also well known for its specimen trees, many examples of which survive on former nursery grounds and around the locality. Of particular note are those such as listed in the catalogue of 1925, Wellingtonia *(Sequoiadendron giganteum)* and the purple beech *(Fagus sylvatica riversii)*, a Rivers development with a deep purple colour, and various weeping trees including ash and willow.

The nursery itself in 1897, the year of Victoria's Diamond Jubilee, is likely to have stretched to its greatest extent in terms of land area, around three hundred and sixty acres, with a large number of employees, perhaps more than one hundred. Some of this land was scattered as there was a holding for an orchard in Redricks Farm area, there were the osier beds down near the Stort and other holdings in the Station road area of town. Most was still concentrated in the west of Sawbridgeworth, in the High Wych area.

Though this was a climactic time in the history of a successful firm, there is a reminder in his Obituaries that Frank Rivers was not an over-ambitious man. The article in *The Gardeners' Chronicle*, clipped and pasted into the scrapbook of Henry R. Rivers, shows Frank Rivers in a different light: 'Francis Rivers was not so much the head of a great and distinguished nursery firm as a genial, honourable, retiring country-gentleman, well-read and one who assimilated what he read. Moreover, he did much experimental work, for which his father, perhaps unavoidably, got the credit...'[4]

Images of the beautiful fruit produced make a most pleasing record of the Nursery's stock at the time. May Rivers, the eldest daughter of Frank

Rivers, was an accomplished artist at a time when all well-bred young women were given art lessons. Her depictions of many fruits she posed for their portraits were used as illustrations in *The Fruit Growers' Guide* by John Wright published in 1892. These accurate watercolours included blossom in order to be used as identifications. Many of her sketches and preliminary drawings survive as does the finished work included in the book.

The new century

When Frank Rivers died in 1899, two of his sons - the eldest, Thomas Alfred Hewitt and the youngest, Henry Somers - took over the management of the Nursery. Thomas Alfred, who directed the growing and outdoor section of the nursery, had spent eight years in America, in Colorado, mining and ranching but had returned to Sawbridgeworth to work with his father in 1894 on the large tracts of land holdings and large stocks of fruit. From an article in *The Garden* of 1902, it seems that he was shaping up to continue the traditions of the firm, the grasp of the market and the search for new varieties.[5]

However, in 1915, not long after he had been invited to join the Fruit

Committee of the Royal Horticultural Society, he died unexpectedly. This was a difficult time in the life of the nation as WWI was just beginning and the turmoil that was to follow and affect all levels of society was reflected in life at the Nursery. Henry, Thomas Alfred's younger brother, had been running the offices of the company but as WWI began, he joined the Royal Fusiliers. At his brother's death, Henry left the army and came back to work at the Nursery, which would have been classed as essential work of national importance.[6]

A Rivers Family photograph with T.A.H. Rivers on the right in exotic garb in the garden of Bonks Hill house.

Reproduced by kind permission of Peter Rivers

Figure 7.4

For the Nursery, WWI marked the end of that prolonged period of growth and stability extending through the eighteenth and nineteenth centuries. Conditions had changed. The large estates with grand gardens and grand horticultural aspirations started being sold off. Ordinary households put in smaller orders. The government required that some of the Rivers land be used for food crops. There were fewer workers available and after the war, fewer returned to take up the old employment. There was more competition from new nurseries and in the absence of a patenting system, newly developed varieties could be reproduced by other firms in a relatively short period.

All of these changes required readjustment of aims. Perhaps the old certainties and belief in the worth of searching for the endless horticultural possibilities generally faltered. A gradual decline in the nursery fortunes set in, with parcels of land eventually being sold off.

However, in the twenty years between the wars, life became quieter again. Rivers continued to be not only a nationally important horticultural firm but very significant locally. Henry S. Rivers continued as managing director until his death in 1935. His daughters, Peggy and Ursula, figure in many of the dramatic photographs taken for advertising features in the 1930s. One of the most alluring shows Peggy in an orchard house, pollinating with a paintbrush. Earlier it would have been a rabbit's tail but as rabbits became more scarce the tool used was a soft paintbrush to transfer pollen from blossom to blossom, necessary in the indoor environment of the glasshouse.

M. D. Rivers, known as Peter, who was the younger son of Thomas Alfred, came into the business with Henry Rivers and became director in

1935. However, he stayed in that post for only three years, emigrating to South Africa in 1938. The last Thomas, Thomas Hall Rivers, trained and working as a civil engineer, followed his brother as director. As he and his family were not then resident at the Nursery, the company was managed for a time by reputable Wisley-trained A.N. Rawes. Tom Rivers visited the Nursery every other Sunday during war-time according to his daughter. [7]

World War II

The dramatic events of WWII were echoed by dramatic events at the Nursery. Bonks Hill House was empty at the time as Thomas Hall Rivers was not yet on site. The army commandeered the house and parked army vehicles in the grounds, cutting off the lower branches of the huge lime tree and pouring spent oil around the roots of the great Wellingtonia near the house, one of those raised and sold widely by the Nursery. This was the same tree that has recently had to be taken down, maybe weakened by its unlikely diet and lightening strikes.[8]

This was a period of great change. More than half of the land had to be used for food crops. Land girls came to work beside the older hands. Mechanical methods of cultivation gradually replaced traditional hand tools and methods. There was a loss of traditional horticultural knowledge as men went off to war. Fuel was rationed so that the citrus fruit and glasshouse cultivation for other delicate fruit was compromised. The glasshouses were getting old, some having been constructed as much as a century before, and all needed maintenance.

In 1948, the last Thomas Rivers returned to Bonks Hill house and the management of the business, leaving his engineering career. Until his death in 1978, he maintained the traditions of the company while accepting the new realities and attempting to move with the times. He retained the family gift for being able to connect personally with his work force, with many fondly remembering his warmth and generosity of spirit. An article from 1950 in *The Gardeners' Chronicle*, describes Tom Rivers at the Nursery. At that time there were one hundred and eighty acres in cultivation. The correspondent speaks of some of the glass houses being reconstructed and of the stock plants of peaches, nectarines, vines and citrus fruit such as oranges, tangerines, lemons and grapefruit being raised under glass. He describes the young trees being trained in the growing areas in various shapes such as fans and espaliers and the fine specimen trees including a huge weeping beech and two purple beeches. The article concludes, 'all

Tom Rivers in the Peach House
Reproduced by kind permission of John Sapsford

Figure 7.5

looked in good heart…and is still going strong'.[9]

Despite this resumption of business as normal in the immediate post-war years, much was changing within the nursery and in the country. In the brief booklet Tom Rivers wrote in 1975 marking two hundred and fifty years of the company's existence, he speaks of some of the major changes.

East Malling

He notes that fruit development research had become the work of professionals at research stations such as East Malling in Kent. Considered in the light of the research and development of new varieties carried out by the successive Thomas Rivers of the nineteenth century - observation and research that had not only determined their positions as major innovators of the times but had made the reputation of the firm - the fact that research had now been transferred to national scientific stations was a huge change. The Rivers Nursery was one of the founder members of East Malling and followed its work closely, adapting new virus free rootstocks as they appeared and in other ways trying to follow new developments in production techniques. East Malling Research Station has itself an interesting history, having been founded in 1913 and continuing through many phases as an important institution today.

Another change was that much of the stock of fruit trees, sent out bare-rooted in winter, was no longer raised in the Nursery grounds, but bought in from a wholesale nursery in Worcestershire. This transfer allowed stock to be raised in disease-proof conditions, and therefore to be the healthiest possible and was now sold in what had become a Rivers retail business.

The realities of the post WWII era - that Tom Rivers was not a dedicated horticulturist in the tradition of the Thomas Rivers of the past and that the company bought in rather than developing their own stock - changed the nature of the Nursery.

However, though discontinuing development of new varieties, and not growing their own stock, the company continued for many years as an important retail catalogue company, selling to a large number of smaller customers as recorded in the order books which survive from the twentieth century in the Hertfordshire County Archives. A garden centre in the new style was added about 1970 to the nursery site off the High Wych road near the office at Wisemans. This was managed for a time by Tom Rivers' son, Nigel. The land area was gradually reduced through sale of different sections until when the final reckoning came, the total amount remaining was about ninety acres.

The end of Rivers Nursery

Before Tom Rivers died in 1978, he said to his daughter Margaret who would become the main director of the business that he wished for the Nursery to continue. The employees who remained, most of them having been long-serving and enthusiastic members of the company workforce over a number of years, wanted and believed the Nursery would continue. However, it no longer occupied the prominent position in the local or national horticulture world it once did. Although there was a garden centre it was not successful on the scale of the modern ones that had sprung up around.

For the company to succeed, a re-imagining of the aims and a large investment in new ideas would have been necessary. It seems that the capital for such a reinvention was not available. Nor was there a family member in position who could make it happen. It came as a bitter blow that such a renowned company would be sold and that nothing would remain of it in the local area except its history. The employees, some of them still living in Rivers' properties, lost their work and some their homes too. Despite disagreements, all the local family concluded selling was necessary. The stockholders, including those family members living abroad, were consulted and with regret agreed to the sale. The community mourned, there were numerous articles in the papers during the period when the company teetered between holding on and continuing or selling, all noting

The Nursery in its glory days: Grapes in the enormous vinery
Reproduced by kind permission of Hertfordshire Archive and Local Studies (D/ERs B90 1/109)

Figure 7. 6

the implications of the loss of such a major company.

However, the sale took place and all of the land remaining and all of the properties were sold to a developer. There was to be nothing left of the great Rivers firm.

Conservation

Tony Slingsby, the last manager, was instrumental in saving two caches of Rivers material. In 1981 he took a heap of papers and artefacts - accounts and order books of the twentieth century, photographs, articles, lithograph plates and the like, whatever was left in the office that had been offered to him by the last Thomas Rivers - to County Hall, Hertford, to be deposited in the Archives. Thus anyone interested today is able to sample some of the Rivers heritage.

In a second effort of conservation he invited Reads Nursery of Norfolk to purchase some of the remaining stock that was likely to be lost. Reads, also a long established family firm, from 1841 to the present day, had been a trading partner with Rivers for many years, each supplying the other with fruit trees as needed when supplies ran low as was the practice among nurseries. Reads came to Rivers in these last days of the company's existence mainly to collect grape vine cuttings. Offered the remaining young citrus plants and some stock citrus trees, Terence Read hesitated and then came back for another visit to take them away. For Reads in the following years the Rivers stock led to a great success, with the fashion for citrus trees in the home conservatory still continuing. 10

The family also sold the Darwin letters which were at the end still in their possession. However, they too are saved and now held in the Darwin correspondence collection of Cambridge University, the originals available to view and now to be read on-line.

Notes

1. 'Obituary Frank Rivers', *The Gardeners' Chronicle*, August 26, 1899.
2. Thomas H. Rivers, *1725 - 1975: 250 Years of Thomas Rivers and Son Ltd. of Sawbridgeworth* (1975).
3. Letter from T.F. Rivers to Mr. T. Dyer, Esq., Jan. 14, 1887, Kew Archives.
4. *The Gardeners' Chronicle*, August 26, 1899.
5. 'Workers among the Flowers and Fruit - T. Alfred H. Rivers', *The Garden*, December 13, 1902, p. 408.
6. 'Obituary, Thomas Alfred Hewitt Rivers', *The Gardeners' Chronicle*, August 5, 1915, p. 109.
7. Margaret Rivers, Recorded Interview, March 30, 2009. John Sapsford.
8. Margaret Rivers. Nigel Rivers Recorded Interview, April 5, 2009.
9. 'Nursery Notes, Messrs. Thomas Rivers and Son Ltd.' *The Gardeners' Chronicle*, July 13, 1950, p. 31.
10. Discussion with Terence Read of Reads Nursery, July 2009.

Wartime Memories of Rivers Nursery and Surroundings
by John Sapsford

'This country is now at war with Germany.' When I heard these words on the radio spoken by Prime Minister Neville Chamberlain on September 3rd 1939, I was seventeen and living with my parents in Weeping Ash bungalow. We had moved there some two years previously when my father had been made general manager of Rivers Nursery. The bungalow, which still exists, is near the junction of High Wych Road with London Road, beside the drive to Bonks Hill House. In 1939, Bonks Hill was unoccupied except for a caretaker, Mr. Churchman and his family. Thomas H. Rivers, who had inherited the house and the firm on the death of his uncle, Henry S. Rivers, was then working as a civil engineer with I.C.I., the chemical giant.

The media had predicted that declaration of war would immediately be followed, or even be preceded, by massive air raids on London and other vital targets. There was an air raid warning sounded soon after the declaration which turned out to be a false alarm. Otherwise September 3rd passed off quietly like any other Sunday. Our first indication that things had changed came quickly when Bonks Hill House was commandeered by the Army to accommodate soldiers of the Royal Army Ordnance Corps who were establishing a supply depot adjacent to nearby Rowney Farm. The first casualty was the gated entrance to the drive. Having hit one gatepost with a lorry, the soldiers cut the posts off at ground level.

Otherwise life in Sawbridgeworth, as in most of Britain, continued quietly, much as before, for nearly a year. The anticipated air raids did not materialise and people had a sense of anti-climax and wondered what all the fuss had been about. Children, hastily evacuated from London into the countryside in the last few days before September 3rd began to drift back home to their parents.

In the Atlantic, however, German submarines were beginning to inflict casualties on merchant ships bringing supplies to Britain. With experience from the 1914-18 war, when similar action had brought the country dangerously close to starvation levels, the Government initiated immediate plans to make this country self-sufficient in food production as rapidly as possible. For Rivers Nursery this meant that areas used to grow fruit trees for three or four years until they were ready for sale were cleared and planted with soft fruits and other crops which would give a more immediate harvest. All of the glasshouses near to the offices and some near Bonks Hill were given up to tomato and cucumber production. The Vinery was retained as was the Citrus House and some of the orchard houses near Bonks Hill.

Working in the Vinery during the War
Reproduced by kind permission of John Sapsford

Figure Sp.1

This all required some extra labour and replacements were needed to cover the loss of younger men who were joining the Services. Many local ladies were recruited to fill the gaps. At harvest time and whenever extra hands were needed the official Women's Land Army was called upon. At peak times later in the war, as many as two hundred ladies were on the Nursery.

In October 1939 I had started work with the Holbrook Machine Tool Company, whose newly built factory was between Harlow Mill and the railway station. (All references to Harlow are to what is now known as Old Harlow, as the new town had not yet been envisaged.) Much of what follows relates to what I saw from the factory, although most would also have been seen from the Nursery.

In May 1940 the war in France erupted as German troops swept through Holland and Belgium into northern France, followed soon by the surrender of France and the evacuation of British troops from Dunkirk. Britain was poised expecting invasion. In July and early August the German Air Force started attacks against airfields and coastal targets in Kent and Sussex.

On the twenty-fourth of August, a loud noise attracted us outside the Holbrook office to see a very large and immaculate formation of German bombers and escorting fighters heading south. No raid alarm had been sounded and my boss had just said they must be British when we heard bombs exploding. Then the warning sounded. This was the first of several raids on North Weald fighter airfield some four miles away. Much later it was officially stated that over two hundred bombs had been dropped causing considerable damage and casualties.

For the next three weeks there were air battles almost every day with the clear skies crisscrossed with vapour trails as our fighters engaged the enemy at high altitude. Raids were again directed against airfields, some on North Weald and other over flying on their way to Duxford, Debden or others to the north. We went out to the shelters, which were on land adjacent to the factory, whenever the alarm was sounded but many, like myself, preferred to stand outside and watch the action. A few days later a Heinkel bomber came straight over us at low level pursued by a Hurricane. Despite the obvious risk from machine gun bullets we stood and cheered. The Heinkel went down just across the valley of the Stort. When I was free, I cycled to find the aircraft on fields which were being prepared for Hunsdon Airfield.

On the third September during the heaviest raid on North Weald, many incendiary bombs were dropped in and around Harlow and an unexploded bomb landed in fields close behind the factory. The biggest scare however was when a Messerschmitt 110 twin engine fighter in flames passed low over us to crash out of control at Churchgate Street. On the same day we saw a Hurricane crash in flames near Hunsdon.

On the seventh September, in the mistaken belief that the British fighter defence had been eliminated, the Germans changed tactics and caught the fighters off guard. Instead of continuing their attacks on airfields they sent a massive daylight raid to attack the dock area of East London. The glow of fires could be clearly seen after dark from the high ground at High Wych and the Germans followed up with the first major night raid. During the next week the Germans found out the hard way that the RAF fighter force was still in good shape. Their losses were so high that they mounted no more large daylight raids and concentrated almost entirely on night attacks. These were less accurate and many stray bombs fell in the countryside, some by aircraft which were unsure of their position, others from planes which had been damaged by anti aircraft fire over London.

In the second half of September bombs fell in Great and Little Hallingbury, Sheering, in fields beside Sheering Lower Road close to the Walter Lawrence factory and at Quickbury Farm. On the night of tenth October, I was walking into Sawbridgeworth escorting my future wife home and had reached the corner of Hoestock Road when I heard the unmistakable sound of a falling bomb. Knowing it must be close, we dropped to the ground just before a loud explosion. This was the bomb which fell in the roadway outside what is now Leventhorpe School and demolished a pair of houses and damaged others. Two adults and three children were killed, the only air raid casualties in the town. On the same night, parachute mines were dropped on marshes near the station and at Hyde Hall.

The night attacks on London continued unabated and I was occasionally sent to Holbrooks's Stratford factory. When I first went there, the streets near the factory were full of terraced houses but a few weeks later they had all gone and the factory stood in isolation. The factory had been shaken many times and the steel uprights were said to be several inches out of true. When I had time to spare I walked in the area toward the docks where the devastation was almost complete. Another time I went further into London two days after a particularly heavy raid. I shall never forget seeing the almost undamaged St. Paul's standing isolated among acres of rubble. Almost all the buildings within about half a mile were either flattened or burnt out shells. Demolition gangs were busy knocking down a few remaining walls that had somehow managed to stay precariously upright. This served to put into perspective the minor inconveniences we had locally.

Bombs continued to fall in this area. In April 1942 Lawrence's factory was attacked with mainly incendiary bombs. The area in which Mosquito aircraft fuselages were being built was very badly damaged. Production was stopped but due to the efforts of Lawrence's own staff deliveries were resumed within six weeks. The factory produced some seventeen hundred Mosquito fuselages during the war. This raid also demonstrated that bureaucracy was still active even in war time. The factory was on the Essex side of the river and the Sawbridgeworth fire brigade were not permitted to attend, despite being ready and waiting in Sheering Mill Lane long before the Essex fire engines arrived.

About the same time a large bomb fell in the corner of Pishiobury Park near to Springhall Lane, the crater of which can still be seen although overgrown with hawthorn scrub. Bombs also fell around Hyde Hall, then being used as the Officers' Mess for the newly established RAF Sawbridgeworth airfield north of Allens Green. Hunsdon airfield was now also in operational service initially as a night fighter base to counter the night raids. At first the aircraft used were Hurricanes and Defiants which had limited success. These were replaced first by Havocs, then by the much more successful Beaufighters and Mosquitoes which were fitted with airborne radars.

An incident that was puzzling at the time was when a small bomb exploded in Pishiobury Park and, next morning, a long length of fine wire was found festooned among the trees. It has since been published that this was a defence idea. The intention was that a British aircraft should fly above, and in front of, of German bomber stream. It would then release a number of small bombs each attached by a long wire to a parachute. The theory was that this would fall slowly and be flown into by a bomber. The wire, caught in the wings, would be dragged back by the parachute thereby lifting the bomb into contact with the plane where it would explode and blow the wing off. Fine in theory, but the sky is a big place and the chances of the wire striking a plane were very small. What was certain however was that the device would fall to earth with considerable risk of, at least, damage to, say, power or telephone lines. The idea was dropped after a few trials. More practical methods of defence against the bombers were being rapidly developed, such as airborne radar, which soon proved their effectiveness. The large scale raids gradually became less frequent but raids on a smaller scale continued.

In the dark days of 1940, we were working twelve hours every day, seven days a week. It was soon realised that to continue this indefinitely was counter productive, so working hours were progressively reduced until by the end of 1941 we were back to more normal hours. With more free time, I joined the High Wych Home Guard, which leads to many more memories, mainly not appropriate here. One, however, is perhaps relevant. Because of my interest in maps and draughting, I was ordered to liase with a regular army officer to prepare a large scale plan of the area around the junction of

Station Road and London Road, showing the type of construction of every building. No reason was quoted at the time but I have since learned that Sawbridgeworth would have been on a major fall-back defence line if the Germans should have made a successful landing on the east coast.

After Pearl Harbour, the Americans joined in the war. This saw the building of many more airfields in Essex and across East Anglia to accommodate the American Air Force. Nearest to us were Stansted and Matching Green. These required large quantities of sand and gravel, much of which came from a pit where the houses of Nursery Fields and Gilders estates are now built.

Perhaps to delay this airfield building, the Germans introduced a new type of bomb, one of the first of which was dropped near the Little Hallingbury Road. This was a canister which opened at altitude to release large numbers of small bomblets which opened small wings and fell slowly to earth much like sycamore seeds. They spread over a considerable area to land without exploding until they were disturbed, when the explosion was sufficient to maim or possibly kill a person. Authority wanted information on the spread pattern of these bombs and asked the police to find and mark the positions. The only large scale maps readily available were owned by the local gas company who used them to record their pipelines. The police came to Holbrooks for help and I was given the job of tracing the maps so that we could make prints.

Soon the Americans arrived and became familiar around the towns though sometimes forgetting which side of the road they should be on. Massive formations of Fortresses and Liberators became a familiar sight over

Vera Maskell and friends at Rivers making the V for Victory sign
Reproduced by kind permission of Vera Maskell
Figure Sp.2

the area as they formed up for raids on Germany. It was soon after this that a new threat appeared. The Germans launched the first of their secret weapons - the V1, more commonly known as the Doodlebug. This unmanned flying bomb used a pulse jet engine which made an unforgettable raucous racket. They flew fairly low on a straight course until the fuel was shut off, when the thing dived to earth and exploded with considerable force. Several exploded in local fields but no lives were lost. However, doodlebugs killed many in London.

Soon after this the Holbrook factory was shaken by a violent explosion without any warning. We soon heard that a large crater had appeared in Parndon Wood. This was one of the first two V2 rockets which were launched from Holland and went well up into the stratosphere at supersonic speeds before completing the parabola to fall on this country. There was no warning of their approach and no way in which they could be intercepted. Many casualties were caused in London. These were not stopped until after landings in France, the advance of our troops had progressed enough to force the launch sites out of range.

Several stray rockets landed in this area without casualties. One of these woke us at Weeping Ash with a tremendous explosion followed by a ground tremor as though something heavy had landed. I went out in the dark to explore but could find nothing. Next morning I went out again and, just beyond where I had walked in the night I found the massive rocket motor of a V2. The explosion we heard must have been the sonic boom (though this term was not yet known) as the rocket re-entered the atmosphere. The warhead carried on and exploded in fields nearer Much Hadham. Authorities looked at the remains and suggested it be buried. It was dragged a short distance to a convenient hold where it was covered over and to the best of my knowledge still remains below the housing development of The Crest.

One last memory of the war remains, which indicated that perhaps it was nearly over. This was the sight of an aerial armada of Stirling bombers towing Horsa and Hadrian gliders passing over the Nursery from Matching to carry airborne troops to consolidate the crossing of the Rhine. We were well and truly on our way into Germany itself.

John Sapsford is the son of Rivers' manager, Arthur Sapsford. Though becoming an engineer, his early years were spent as part of the Rivers community. He has been generous in sharing his knowledge of the Nursery and has been invaluable as an advisor to the group restoring the orchard.

Memories of Rivers Nursery and Rural Sawbridgeworth
by Eric Willison

Three generations of my family worked at Rivers Nursery. The first was William Camp (1847 - 1928). Though coming from two generations of Sawbridgeworth shoemakers, William became a distinguished nurseryman, working for the Veitch Nursery in Chelsea as well as Rivers, where he eventually became general manager around the turn of the century at a time when the fortunes and reputation of the business were at their highest. He lived at Newports, a large house near the Nursery along High Wych road.

Newports

c. 1908

Reproduced by kind permission of Eric Willison

Figure W.1

His son, Edwin Camp (1876 - 1943), followed him into employment at the nursery. As well as a notable nurseryman, he was a distinguished beekeeper and won many awards for his honey. Edwin realized the need for bees in pollinating the fruit. He had his own orchard in High Wych with his favourite fruit trees - Early Rivers Plum, Victoria Plum, Conference Pear, Merryweather Damson and many others. He taught women and boys at Rivers Nursery during WWII all the nursery skills required for propagation and cultivation. These included budding, grafting, the striking of cuttings and potting up.

My grandfather and great-grandfather were both in great demand around the country as the large landowners called on them for their expertise and advice as to which fruit trees to plant and which soil conditions were necessary.

Edwin's son, William George Camp (1911 - 2002) also came into Rivers' employment as a nurseryman and clerk. Later he became the sub-postmaster at High Wych.

I was born in 1942. From the age of eight I remember accompanying my uncle William to check the coke boilers at the weekend. I can remember the wonderful smell of a humid greenhouse such as the vine and peach house. The aroma of ripe peaches was unforgettable. I was allowed to gather those that were fallen. My uncle told me the vine was planted outside the house and trained inside. When a horse died, it would be buried against the roots to give it the nutrients it required over many years. There used to be a submerged tank in the green house, catching water from the roof, always at the correct temperature for watering. It had lots of frogs and creepy crawlies in it which I found fascinating.

The nurserymen could tell if a pot was dry by tapping the side with a stick as they walked by. A pot was much better dry than over-watered. Nurserymen were skilled at grafting and budding onto stock. Evidence of sharpening their knives on the way to work in the morning can be seen on the backwater bridge at Harlow Mill, where the sandstone copings are worn away.

Growing skills were part of

Edwin Camp in a glasshouse
Reproduced by kind permission of Eric Willison
Figure W.2

the curriculum at Sawbridgeworth Secondary Modern School, located off Sheering Mill Lane. Whilst I was at school we had a thriving garden area, complete with bee hives. We were taught how to dig, propagate, sow and harvest. Even at my junior school, we were shown how to strike cuttings and sow seeds and plant. I can point to a tree now in High Wych that I planted in 1950, so much better than today's youths who sometimes prefer to break trees down!

A lot of the nurserymen lived very near the Nursery at The Hand & Crown terrace, Wisemans Gardens or at High Wych. The Barnards lived in the cottages at the entrance to Rivers, as did Nellie Barnard, the village school mistress. The Hand & Crown was a meeting place for many locals including the village youth. The landlord, Percy Needham, allowed the village youth to use his upstairs room over the bar.

As well as the Wisemans entrance to the nursery, there continued to be another, off Bonks Hill. In front of Bonks Hill House is a brick wall with a siding which led up to the seed and fruit sheds. My uncle William Camp said it was a collection point when fruit used to go to market, I think Covent Garden. He also said that Chivers, the marmalade makers, used to return the fruit seed for propagation.

Alf Dedman took care of the horses which were stabled at the Rivers entrance at Wisemans. During the holidays, Alf would give us rides on the hay cart. The horses and cart were kept in the yard opposite the offices and Alf lived in the Hand Terrace. It was amazing sitting on top of the cart looking down on the cart horse. Rivers had two horses, originally used for ploughing. They were put out to graze in a field at the new entrance to Rivers along High Wych Road. At that time the entrance was by way of a five barred gate. I remember once when we had to call Alf out to untangle his horses from some barbed wire. It was a terrible ordeal as I remember.

Just inside the gate was a sizeable pond where we used to catch great crested newts using cotton with a little worm on the end. When a newt ate the worm you hoisted it

Edwin Camp's bee
keeping equipment
1910
Reproduced by kind permission
of Eric Willison

Figure W.4

out. There were lots of owls around that field in the trees bordering it. In the far corner of the field behind Sweetbriars cottages was a rabbit warren. The nurserymen used to bring their ferrets and chase them out.

Further up the High Wych Road was another entrance to the straw stack yard. Every summer we would go ratting when the threshing of the corn took place and all the rats would run across the field. At harvest time when the corn was put in stooks to dry, we would go gleaning for our chickens. After harvesting the field would be ploughed up with steam ploughs, right up to Windmill Bungalow. A steam plough would be positioned either side of the field and then the plough would be wound back and forth on a cable between them. Three men were involved, one on each engine and one on the plough.

At one time my uncle had some fifteen bee hives and I can remember on occasions being chased by a rogue swarm that had not settled in. The only way to avoid them was to dive through some undergrowth. If we saw a swarm flying over we would go out with the hose to spray it to encourage it to settle, especially in May. Hence the proverb, 'A swarm in May is worth a load of hay; a swarm in June is worth a silver spoon; but a swarm in July is not worth a fly'—for it is then too late to store up honey before the flowers begin to fade.

I was brought up with the distinctive smell of the fruit shed where there were apples and pears, both kept on racks to allow air flow and space for the Conference pears to ripen. The smell of honey, bees wax and the strong smell of burnt paper from the smoke puffer are all unforgettable.

It was inevitable that Rivers Nursery would close, what with a shortage of horticultural skills, mismanagement and Harlow New Town on the doorstep offering better working conditions and garden products. The greenhouses were reaching the end of their life span during my youth. As in most other nurseries of that period, every Rivers greenhouse was made of softwood and the timber rotted and the glass fell out. Selling out for development was the most profitable option.

In the early 1950's and for a number of years after, I saw many of our green areas in High Wych and Sawbridgeworth disappearing. Our allotments went for the Wychford Drive estate, opposite Wiseman's Gardens on the High Wych Road as did The Hand & Crown Lane field. Our chicken farm became the Rowney Wood and Wheatley Close estates. An area of natural beauty, Falconers Park, was developed by Helmer &

Dyer. A chicken farm and piggery became East Park estate. Much of Rivers Nursery was sold to Helmer & Dyer for The Crest and Gilders. Our farm land east of Sawbridgeworth went for the Vantorts estate.

There are still areas of Sawbridgeworth where people seek to build. We must preserve Rivers Orchard and adjoining areas. Once a green area is built on, it is lost forever.

Eric Willison is the great grandson of the distinguished Rivers Nursery manager, William Camp. He has lived in Sawbridgeworth all his life.

Chapter Eight

The End of Rivers Nursery
An Orchard is Rescued

By the end of the 1980s the sense of outrage at the closure of that local institution - Rivers Nursery - had been replaced by nostalgia. Articles in the local press were being published about the Nursery as one of the glories of the past, a firm that had brought renown to the area. Against that background as the hospital to be called Rivers was erected on former nursery land, a remainder of the property not to be immediately built upon was given into the control of East Hertfordshire District Council (EHDC) by leasehold for twenty years, until the end of 2009. This was to be used by permission of the Council for the local community.

Rescue and restoration

Why should the district council have taken on this lease, an unusual commitment? Looking back, it is possible to see a number of forces in play. Rivers land was and continues to be in the Green Belt. All councils have an obligation to see that inappropriate development is not allowed to take place there. The local councillors were responding to the sense of loss experienced by the community and therefore made a strong case for the retention of some land memorialising the Nursery. If that could provide green space, always a popular concept, especially within a Green Belt area, so much the better. While making a forceful argument for the lease enhanced their own popularity, the twenty year term meant that a final decision about land use could be postponed until a time when most councillors in post would have been replaced by others, who would be able to review options which might have appeared in the meanwhile. In addition, the decision to take on a lease would not cost EHDC money, as the rent was a token one (as was to be the cost to developers taking back the land at the end of the lease). Supporting initiatives to enhance the state of the land, such as restoring the orchard, would also not require council expenditure as organisers could apply for grants from discrete pots of money, some supported by national funding. In the event, the strong case urged by local councillors won the day and the lease was taken on. The lease covers an area of about forty acres in total.

To make the best of what had now in effect become community property there had to be a sense of purpose. Some of land, the open field area at the end of the Crest neighbourhood, and meadowland formerly the site of soft fruit beds, was left as found. It would be rough grassland to be kept mowed and generally free of undergrowth by EHDC and was welcomed as open space and kick-about area in an increasingly urbanised locality. The meadow land, measuring about fourteen acres, had as it naturalised over the years an important function as a wildflower site and refuge and attraction for wildlife, butterflies and moths in particular as butterfly surveys faithfully carried out over the years testify.

On another section of nearly five acres just to the west of the site of the hospital buildings, there was what seemed to be an overgrown orchard. Colonized by bramble, hawthorn, wild cherry and the like, no longer productive of fruit, no longer even a good haven for wildlife, it was a wilderness, ready to be altogether lost. This, research showed, was the remainder of a Rivers orchard. That it was an orchard was evident from the orderly planting but the trees were old and their original use was not clear. What was known was that Rivers did not set orchards to bear fruit which could be sold at markets, but that the trees planted had other uses, such as being mother trees providing propagation material or serving as a show orchard to give customers an idea of what the trees they were going to buy

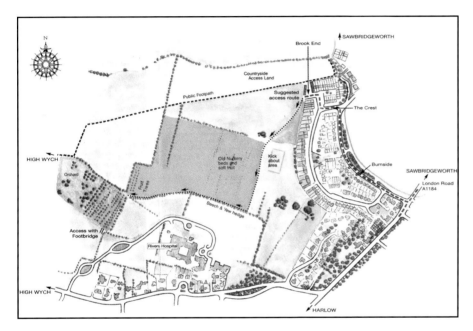

Map of the Rivers
Nursery Site and
Orchard
as it appears in 2009 with the
restored Orchard area shaded in
green and the meadowland in blue

Figure 8.1

might become. Any fruit which might be produced was then not wasted, but
was sold or used in horticultural shows. This orchard had been abandoned
for some time.

There was a notion that perhaps, whatever the original identity of the
orchard, it might now be restored to serve a dual function: as a community
facility and as a memorial for the great Nursery. As this idea gained
currency, various individuals and bodies began to show interest and offer
support. By the end of 1995, Diana Richards, a local resident and site ranger
for the Countryside Management Service and Susan Clark, then working as a
Rural Enterprise project officer, had joined forces to work out a plan for

orchard restoration and to recruit volunteers while at the same time gaining the interest and support of the general local community. Their work was to have the backing of EHDC.

As the two began to work together, they found that a restored orchard would fit into a growing network of community orchard and countryside development movements which could offer support of various kinds. Initial advice came from such organisations as Common Ground, the Herts and Middlesex Wildlife Trust and the Countryside Management Service. These kinds of bodies had grown important as not only locally but nationally the rural way of life had declined with the loss of farming land to development. Orchards once found commonly in all villages, a necessary part of ordinary food production but providing as well an aesthetic environment and wildlife haven, were rapidly disappearing just as had happened in Sawbridgeworth. From these movements could be gained all sorts of ideas for developing a site and vocal encouragement as well as ideas for finding financial support.

Just as important for a restoration process was the recruitment of volunteers. From the first calls, volunteers came, willing and hard-working year after year, partly captured by the vision of the community space growing around them and the idea of learning new skills, partly for the fellowship and fun of the activities, partly from the notion of service and trust in the two main organisers. These were for the most part older people. Families and children were attracted when activities such as an annual Wassailing - in the ancient tradition of singing, apple tree blessing and bonfires in January at Twelfth Night - and Apple Day - showing the town the not-to-be-found-in-supermarkets bounty of the newly productive trees - were organised. Some then became involved in the work of orchard maintenance.

In addition to talking to all youth groups and their leaders such as the local Scouts, the organisers made an effort to involve the local schools

Apple bobbing in 1998 at the Rivers Orchard Apple Day held at Church House Sawbridgeworth
Reproduced by kind permission of the *Citizen*

Figure 8.2

realising that school children had largely lost the sense of connection to the countryside around them and that their understanding of the sources of their food was diminished. As some of the volunteers were on the governing boards of schools, connections with the restored orchard were made easier. Schools were invited to walk into the place and to see the trees, pick the fruit in season, write about their visits, photograph and draw and while there hear the history of the Rivers Nursery. Diana Richards began giving talks about the Rivers Nursery Orchard as it became known to community groups to raise awareness, gain participation and bring in a little cash for buying equipment and the like.

Susan Clark drew up a Management Plan for the site detailing the objectives of the work of restoration in prospect. These were: 'to enhance the historic features; to improve facilities for low use informal recreation; to enhance the landscape value of the site to screen more effectively existing and future developments; to enhance the reputations of the Rural Enterprise Project; East Hertfordshire District Council; Sawbridgeworth Town Council and the Countryside Management Service'. Proposals were made to cover a ten year period of work to be carried out from 1996, including conserving the existing trees, replacing lost trees, maintaining and extending the hedgerows, restoring the ditch to provide aquatic habitat and providing public access. (*Rivers Nursery Site Management Plan*, July 1996, prepared by Susan Clark) Once volunteers were ready to work, funding their efforts was essential. An initial grant of £3000 was secured and then further grants were applied for including a Countryside Stewardship Grant designed to provide significant on-going funding.

The on-the-ground restoration effort began in 1996 with clearing a path for a protective beech hedge, following the practice of the Nursery in the past, using this barrier as it grew to create a micro-climate, protecting the trees from the harsher winds on what is a relatively high position and ameliorate the cold and damp. A long beech and yew hedge leading from the field area had survived and the new one was planned to continue the protection it offered. Later a further hedge was planted along the western edge of the restored nursery defining the space and setting it off from the farmland stretching beyond. The hedges signalled to walkers on the public footpaths and to farmers that a cultivated area was within.

With the clearing of scrub from around the fruit trees and for the hedge underway, growths of native species of wild plants had appeared in response to the improved conditions. Early efforts were made to promote the natural biodiversity of the area as part of creating a community space. Volunteers removed bee orchids under threat in the exposed areas to replant in more sheltered positions in 1996. Other plants such as vetchling appeared in the now cut grass around the trees, offering the further pleasure of old grassland wild flowers in the midst of the trees. With the plants came the wildlife - butterflies and moths and other insects, small mammals and amphibians. The Rivers Orchard with the meadowlands beyond became part of a corridor for wildlife now understood to be necessary in the urbanised or intensively farmed areas remaining near Sawbridgeworth. All of these incomers were actively welcomed. The newly restored orchard was to be managed in an organic manner, with no pesticides used even to deter the thick growth at the bases of the trees struggling to regain fruitfulness or artificial fertilizers. With this policy went the effort to raise awareness of what green spaces such as this actively managed, organic orchard offered in saving a piece of ancient countryside in what was still Green Belt land.

Eventually, after years of tearing the trees from the wilderness, an orderly pattern of fruitful trees had emerged, undergrown with grass interspersed with flowers, the ditch once again cleared for drainage, regular maintenance established, regular picking organised, bee hives set to the edge for pollination and honey. An annual sequence of events was established to celebrate the stages in the fruit growing year.

The Rivers Nursery Orchard had gained recognition and the local community valued the new place. Though the effort to make it known to all would never be completed nor the search for new volunteers, yet all of the

The Orchard in bloom
Photograph Susan Clarke
Figure 8.3

publicity - given by the local media and beyond, the word of mouth information, the website and continuous networking with other community groups - had won it a following. Those cited in the management plan: the local and district councils and the Rural Enterprise Project, had indeed gained public recognition for their conservation efforts. Diana Richards was co-opted onto the local council in 1996 and continued being elected to local and district councils and was in a good position to argue the value of the newly restored site. There was no opposition to its existence and except for some incidents of vandalism, people have respected the site.

A natural extension of the development of a beautiful place was offering the new site as inspiration to artists and writers. Art days of various kinds were promoted. Drawing, painting, weaving and an animated live performance tour and the like have taken place in the orchard. In 2002-3 a year long Arts project, using the orchard as the subject of verse and music, was supported by a grant from EHDC.

Archive

From 2000, the documents and artefacts discovered in finding out about the place were gathered to start an Archive, housed in Church House in the centre of Sawbridgeworth. Not only has information from past eras been collected, drawing on the rich resources of the County Archives and the Lindley Library for example, but a record of on-going events in the redevelopment of the orchard site is kept. This search for material to make a portrait of the place and develop an understanding of its significance has culminated in the oral history project of 2008 - 2009. By means of the grant from Awards for All, the Orchard team has been able to capture more of the memories of local people who had a connection to the Nursery or to its restoration. These fragile remembrances which all too easily go unheard help put in place some kind of rounded appreciation of what the place has meant over the years. Recorded in peoples' own voices, these perceptions are as safe as they can be.

Twenty years on

Recently with the structure better in place, there is a new initiative in the development of the orchard site. A mighty effort is being made to name the varieties of fruit trees. When the orchard was first being restored little could be discovered as the standing trees, older or younger, had in nearly all instances lost their identification tags. No past records were found as it seemed that the family had not over the years preserved the company books. Records of tree varieties used to fill gaps were not fully available even from the recent restoration period. Therefore the newly reformed volunteer group, known from 2007 as the Rivers Nursery Site and Orchard Group (following on from the Friends of Rivers Orchard) made determining the varieties a priority. If the names could be found, more of the history of Rivers' developments could be followed and more of the value of the present Orchard site understood. The East of England Apples and Orchards Group (EEAOP) has been the chief support in that search, bringing teams of knowledgeable people, experienced with comparing the multitudes of possible varieties. Slowly a full roster of identification is being compiled, not only for apples and pears but also for the more recondite plums and cherries.

The significance of the present day Nursery Orchard

Those involved in the political decision to take the undeveloped land on the Rivers site into the ownership of EHDC for twenty years have for the most part left the government arena. The two original organisers of the restoration effort have also left the Orchard team, leaving the management of the site to others. What now exists in 2009 is a green space that has much significance in a number of ways. It is also now post 2009 facing an uncertain future. Before the end of this year EHDC is due to consider its leasehold on the site now that the twenty period it covered is ending. While the efforts put in on behalf of the community to restore the site and make it available for all kinds of uses have raised its profile and made it valuable, it may after all be lost. Why should it be saved?

A Rivers collection of fruit trees

As a site, it would not have been worth working with were it not for the Rivers Nursery connection. It is a memorial to a world-renowned horticultural firm, with many discoveries and new cultivars in the list of Rivers' achievements. So too it is a memorial to a most important and long enduring local business, employing over the centuries hundreds of local people.

As an orchard, it does and should exist as a Rivers Orchard. Discussion and study of a 1949 aerial photograph and testimony gathered during the oral history project has led recently to clearer understanding of its layout. The plums and cherries on the western end of the site are perhaps survivors of an experimental collection. The varieties have not yet been identified but they may yield information of great interest to those tracing the development of cultivars over the centuries in this country. Like the other trees on the eastern section of land, mainly apples and pears, they were for the most part planted post WWII. These now heavily fruiting trees reflect what was being propagated and sold from the Nursery in the nineteen fifties. This entire collection has intrinsic historical interest.

To maintain a fruitful orchard, the Orchard group continues to infill gaps left as trees die with local varieties or with a new emphasis on maintaining a collection of varieties the Nursery stocked to sell as noted from the Rivers catalogues. Though Rivers sold many varieties of apples, the Nursery did not in fact develop many apple cultivars, choosing to focus more on pears,

Ashmead's Kernel, one
of the many historic
varieties in the orchard
Photograph Eugene Keddy
Figure 8.4

plums and glasshouse fruit. As there are no more glasshouses, the emphasis
in the present orchard is on apples for their ease of cultivation in outdoor
local conditions, with many pears and plums too.

Community orchard, green space, wildlife haven

That the Orchard is now a community orchard is another aspect of its
present identity. As such it is a green space or an ecological treasure of a

specific kind, with a cultivated environment consistent with a certain kind of biodiversity. The orchard linking with the adjacent meadowlands beyond, promotes and protects wild plants and creatures. There is a specific seasonal element to the appeal of the orchard as it offers for all to appreciate the stages in the fruit growing year from bare-branched winter on to uplifting spring blossom then to autumn fruit. It is the only large local orchard left. It is used as open space for walking and enjoying on a daily basis by local people. Others come from further away on picking days and activity days such as Wassail or maintenance days where people enjoy turning up to help. Still others are able to see and purchase historic fruit varieties in town on Apple Day. Schools can make use of it for fulfilling their environmental and local curriculum requirements so that the orchard serves definite education functions.

What is important for its identity as a community orchard is that it exemplifies good green practices and emphasises the value and taste of varieties lost from our usual food suppliers. It serves to remind us that it is not necessary to look to supermarkets to provide all of our food. The land can produce now in the traditional way fruit that has perhaps a less glamorous and uniform appearance but more flavour and more range of flavour to be plucked from trees of old varieties in our own gardens. As community orchard it is part of the movement reminding people that local products are available and that their quality, fresh from the source, is healthier and instantly available. The government initiatives to promote healthier eating habits and pleasant natural exercise for an increasingly obese population also direct attention to what the orchard offers.

A Remainder of the Ancient Countryside

What is the orchard's significance? Look at its location - its setting in the Green Belt, in a fast-changing landscape adjacent to a number of remaining farms. Most of all, the orchard and meadow beyond serve as a memorial to the fertile land which, from the start of the era of cultivation in human prehistory, provided the livelihood of local residents, formed their identity and determined the dominant rural way of life.

Identification of Fruits at Rivers Nursery Orchard
by Eugene Keddy

Soon after I joined the then Friends of Rivers Group, I asked if the trees, which numbered over five hundred, had been mapped since restoration work began in 1995 or even before that date. I discovered that some earlier records had been made but that very little of this work remained. Some apple trees still had numbered plastic labels on them but only a handful were named. I offered to make a new and very full mapping of the entire orchard which would entail labelling apples, pears, plums and cherries.

Surveying trees in Rivers Orchard

Reproduced by kind permission of Martin Skipper

Figure K.1

I started this work in the early part of 2005. I gave each tree a row letter and number: e.g. 5A was an apple tree which I named Felicity as it was the first apple tree that I had ever pruned 'properly'. Full records were made and transferred to computer records taking the usual security precautions.

The next step was obvious. We needed to find experts to identify the many fruit varieties, starting with apples, of which there were two hundred and twenty established and over fifty young 'replacement' trees. Our voluntary group was delighted that Martin Skipper (Chairman) and his team from the East of England Apples and Orchard Project agreed to undertake this specialist work on our behalf.

Sunday, 18th September 2005 was the date set aside as fruit identification day. An early decision was made that EEAOP would look as a group at each tree in turn. They would work row by row following my numbering system. My job was to use an extendable apple-picker to take three specimens with the stipulation that they were taken from different parts of each tree and hand them to our experts who studied their shape, size, colour, lenticels, leaves, eyes, and basins. Some of the 'trickier' specimens were tasted before decisions were made. Martin Skipper, Bob Lever, Clare Stimson, Kevin Browne, Debbie Bryant and Paul Read identified over twenty-five different varieties. Especially difficult cases were bagged-up with very careful

The Thomas Rivers apple variety
Photograph Eugene Keddy
Figure K.2

labelling and taken away by Martin and his team for further consideration. At the end of the day there was a huge sense of achievement. We could now tell anyone who was interested the names of most of our apple trees. Imagine our delight when we were told by the experts that the fruits growing on trees numbered N16 and N17 were the eponymous Thomas Rivers apples!

The young trees were not part of that day's work as they were without fruit in most cases. Sometime later, I decided to follow my 'amateur pomologist's' nose and attempt to find out the names of the young trees. I looked carefully at the base of the trees and very gingerly lifted their guards. In most cases I was lucky enough to find their original labels, still legible, at the bottom of the trees. This whole procedure was most satisfying. Discoveries included cider varieties such as Kingston Black and Dunkerton's Late. I was particularly intrigued by Pitmaston Pineapple and Lemon Pippin. I copied these new varieties to my gridsheets and converted all records to my computer.

Our re-constituted group RNSOG (Rivers Nursery Site and Orchard Group) could now decide which heritage apple varieties to plant in the empty spaces in the orchard. Naturally, we chose to increase our stock of Thomas Rivers and other Hertfordshire varieties.

There are now almost six hundred fruit trees in Rivers Nursery Orchard. We still have gaps to fill! Our identification processes have shown us what a rich heritage we have. There are sixty-five different varieties of apples. There are two hundred and twenty established trees alongside seventy-eight younger ones. In his book Apples- A Field Guide, Michael Clark describes one hundred and twenty-two varieties in full detail with illustrations. Forty of these can be found in Rivers Orchard. Interesting varieties in the orchard include Devonshire Quarrenden, Ecklinville Seedling and Emneth Early. Speciality apples raised by Thomas Rivers include Rivers Early Peach, Prince Edward, Rivers Nonsuch and Faerie Queen.

We still await definitive results of our fairly recent plum identification day. What is known to date is that there are ninety-six established trees and twenty-four new ones. They include Czar, Monarch, Rivers Early Prolific, Merryweather and White Bullace.

Some labels have been discovered on younger pear trees to indicate that the following varieties are present: Conference, Concorde, Fertility, Merton Pride, Doyenne de Comice, Magnate, Louise Bonne d'Avranches and Glou Morceau.

Cherries are next to be identified. There are sixty-five established tree with twenty-two younger ones. Hopefully, all trees will be fully recorded in the near future.

Eugene Keddy is a former primary school headteacher who has lived in Sawbridgeworth
for twenty-eight years.

Hedges and their Importance on the Rivers Nursery Site
by Joseph Fitzgerald

Hedges are admired for their aesthetic beauty and elegance or viewed as blight on the landscape impeding increased crop production, depending on the era in which we live. The vast destruction of hedgerows to open up land for food production through two world wars is well documented. Since 1945, a further estimated three hundred thousand miles of hedgerows have disappeared. This seismic change in land use was acutely felt at the Thomas Rivers Nursery where large tracts were converted out of horticultural engagement to agricultural use, by government decree.

Recent surveys suggest that the post war hedgerow decline has slowed and in some areas the trend has been reversed. With a renewed interest in sustainability and biodiversity back in the public domain the status of the humble hedge is also back in discussion and a closer look at these landscape icons will not disappoint. The third Thomas Rivers (1798 - 1877) had an early appreciation of their positive contribution to his horticultural enterprise endeavours. as we will see later.

Hedges, a traditional part of the landscape, have co-existed with agriculture since the earliest days of farming methods. They have had and continue to fulfil multitudinous roles, from legal boundaries to barriers providing corridors for wildlife and sustaining habitats for large varieties of species. They have an aesthetic quality, are responsible for micro-climates and other environmental influences on fruit and food crops and combined with ditches or sited on woodland edges, they provide succour to plants, birds, mammals and invertebrates, including pests and predators. The hedge is a reciprocal ecological landscape structure, providing the right environmental ingredients for plant species to advance that would die in open land, which in turn attract insects that feed visiting birds, that roost, rest and reproduce in ideal surroundings and disperse fruits and seeds ensuring cyclical development. Leaf litter and foraging mammals add to this rich eco mix.

Wind speed at the top and either side of the hedge has a demonstrable impact on insect populations and the spread of wind borne particles of the good and not so good varieties coupled with modulating environmental forces spread effects to surprising distances. The hedge not only encloses, in its original meaning, but provides, expands and protects.

In the eleventh edition (1863) of The Orchard House, Thomas Rivers talks about variations on his theme of 'Cultivation of Fruit Trees under Glass'. He refers to the beech hedges he planted in the 1830s, initially for shelter from the prevailing south west winds and by coincidence and convenience evolving into lean-to houses when the hedge had matured to a height of about eight feet. The dryness of the soil, capture of the sun's energy and regulation of the air provided winter protection and a climate in the summer which he described as delightful in the presence of tea scented roses and shrubs. His variations expanded and he grew hedges to form

A Rivers beech hedge in 1953
Reproduced by kind permission of *Amateure Gardening* Magazine

Figure F.1

walls on all sides of his small orchard houses, choosing yew, beech and Siberian Arbor Vitae to form compact hedges. These were covered with a glass roof, with any heavy rain water dripping directly through the hedge. Experimentation continued with the deliberate placement of beech hedges parallel and adjacent to the Vinery, the Citrus House and assorted orchard houses.

We could speculate with some confidence that he had an advanced grasp of the characteristics of airflow regulation, something we currently allocate millions to perfecting in wind tunnels. He put the theory into practice that more heat is lost from greenhouses by higher external wind speeds and not just by lowest temperatures.

The beneficial outcomes of his innovative inputs are many. Air percolated evenly through his hedges, reducing the need for additional vents and heat regulation. It was possible to stagger the ripening of apricots and peaches, thereby extending the season. Plants that enjoyed harsh environments thrived in the hedge-dried soils. In winter trees and shrubs could be moved in to avoid the frosts and in summer delicate exotic plants could be protected from sudden summer downpours.

The neatly clipped walls of these houses were pleasing to the eye and the aromas and atmosphere within were a 'perfect promenade for persons in delicate health' in Victorian times. The current demonstration nursery orchard that remains with its hedge enclosure has a definite pleasing atmosphere and a micro-climate all of its own.

Hedgerows provide a living historical record of our use of the countryside and this is self evident in the remnants of the Rivers nursery site today. Whilst many of the original land divisions are gone without trace, we do have significant hedgerows and ditches making a vital contribution to the ecological balance.

The existing beech hedge, Fagus Sylvatica, is a prime and prized example of this contribution. The leaves start the season as yellow green, then turn a shiny dark green and the rich brown leaves of autumn last through most of the winter. Native to southern England, it is used more in horticultural and decorative landscapes as the hedge is attractive to grazing livestock. In strong sunlight and on windy days standing next to the dense foliage of the beech hedge gives you a clear indication of the rich variety of its habitat and its exceptional thermo–regulation properties.

The demonstration nursery orchard is surrounded by a woodland edge ditch on one side and dense hedgerows for the majority of the other three. The important contribution to the different animal and plant species of these landscape features cannot be over emphasised. The ditch, used originally as crop land run-off is maintained to attain the right balance between silting and erosion, achieving the right level of ditch vegetation and ensuring water flow conserves rather than disperses the invertebrates that thrive there. The ditch provides an excellent reference point and travelling corridor for various species including large mammals transiting from one habitat to another.

In the environs of a traditional orchard the presence of dead and decaying wood is a vital habitat for a variety of beetle named the noble chafer. Supported by the fact that the site is managed to organic principles means that the impact of herbicides, insecticides and spraying regimes is reduced to a minimum. The role of hedges as a barrier in this process is now a well studied topic.

The hedgerows around and external to the orchard proper are populated with occasional fruit trees and shrubs whose seeds have arrived either by wind transport, resting or feeding birds or passing mammals. Different species of birds use different sectors of the hedges for different functions and this is very evident on the site today. Resting, roosting, and song posts and nesting sites in perfectly drilled tree trunk holes are easily seen. In turn the wild fruits such as blackberries, crab apples as well as the windfalls from the rows of fruits trees provide an excellent resource for autumn and over wintering wildlife. More than twenty of the British butterfly species breed in hedgerows and evidence from recorders on the site confirms the presence of a healthy population of a wide variety of species.

As we look forward to the future conservation objectives for this historical Rivers Nursery site, we need to stop and dwell for a moment on the uniqueness of its hedges, this living landmark, that we daily take for granted. The hedgerows on the site and their distinctive yet different qualities need our care, conservation and commitment. Their general reciprocal role needs greater understanding and their functions as light filters and environmental force modulators needs greater study. Hedges and their often associated ditches provide a whole range of habitats and several climates in one small area. It is for social, economic and ecological objectives that we have a duty to sustain and strengthen this environmental treasure for future generations.

Joseph Fitzgerald is a key member of a number of local organisations, including the Sawbridgeworth Town Partnership. He joined the group restoring Rivers Nursery Orchard in 2004.

The Rescued Orchard and the Rivers Heritage
by Paul Read

Many thousands of old orchard sites have been lost throughout the UK over the last fifty years, in particular those that had a high biodiversity value due to low chemical input and old trees, and also those with high clonal diversity. Many of these are termed today 'traditional orchards', small, many less than an acre (O.4ha), and their form - tree size, ground cover, hedges, fruit species, varieties and tree management - is often typical of a local or regional style. In some counties this once common habitat has been reduced by over 90% in the last fifty years, much of it more recently. In 2007 'Traditional Orchards' became a UK Priority Habitat under the UK Biodiversity regulations, like hay meadows and ancient woodland, and all counties are required to document and endeavour to protect their remaining examples. These county surveys have begun in many counties. Final reports, statements and inventory on all Priority Habitats will be available to planning authorities as a mechanism to assist in their protection. Some local council and national funds are specifically set aside for orchard management, restoration, replanting and recreation, including some county council countryside enhancement funds, Big Lottery grants, DEFRA/NE Stewardship grants, and National Trust managed grants.

Rivers Nursery Orchard is a traditional orchard under this definition. Its size and clonal diversity alone give it national significance, even though many trees are still unidentified - tree surveying may continue for many years - and the wildlife diversity has yet to be properly surveyed and reported.

The Orchard's Origins

The orchard still on the old Rivers Nursery site is not just a few rows of trees, and it wasn't planted as a commercial orchard for its fruit crop. In all likelihood it wasn't planted for its fruit at all. By old orchard standards it is not old although old fruit trees aren't old by comparison with most woodland trees - an ancient apple can be less than one hundred years old, and old plum just fifty, an old pear grafted onto pear rootstock maybe two hundred, on quince rootstock just forty. The trees planted by

Rivers Nursery in this orchard were not all planted at once. One section, almost entirely apples with some pears, was planted not long before 1949 when the photograph below was taken, and the rest including plums and cherries sometime later. The last trees were set out before 1970 when Rivers ceased to propagate its own stock, and started to buy in fruit trees for its garden centre.

There are over one hundred and fifty varieties of tree fruit, apples, cherries, pears and plums - and I mustn't forget the one apricot; the largest number of any one variety appears to be twenty-eight trees, with some varieties only represented by a single tree.

Aerial photograph of 1949, with orchard area in centre and High Wych road in the foreground.

The orchard site shows as a lighter area with almost all the trees planted, except the the last four rows of gages and cherry plums which were planted later. Reproduced by kind permission of John Sapsford

Figure R.1

So why was it planted, what was it for, and why these varieties particular, and why not some of the many others the nursery propagated and sold over the years?

Thirty, forty years ago there were a number of old nursery companies still in existence in England. I did not visit Rivers when it was operational, but I remember Scott's in Devon, Hillier's in Hampshire and Nottcutt's in Suffolk in the 1960s. These tree nurseries, which the public rarely saw beyond the front office, although this would have been relaxed by the 1970s, were amazing places. They appeared to have, and probably had, grown from a single location; a house, some farm buildings, a few sheds, and slowly developed outwards – greenhouses, more sheds, stables turned into garages for tractors, potting and grafting sheds, later polytunnels, innumerable propagation and growing-on beds and everywhere, in a corner, at the end of a bed, in a row beside a path or track, were trees, large, small, many distorted by being raided for propagation material, some ancient and massive, overshadowing the beds.

It seems that Rivers Nursery was just like this in its day, a site planted and slowly growing and developing over more than two hundred and fifty years, a medley of fields, beds, buildings and trees, the scattered source of the propagation material for the nursery, replaced occasionally, sometimes with more than one tree of the varieties that were popular. In some nurseries these trees, the source of wood and buds for propagation were called mother trees. By the time the nursery site was put up for sale from 1982 the under used areas had probably been descending into bramble and a scrub of tree seedlings for a long time.

Fruit Cultivars

It has been understood for centuries, a millennia even, that many, or most, fruit varieties are clones, that is that they are selected single individuals that must be propagated vegetatively (and not by seed, which usually produces a new individual with combined characters of the parents) to retain their essential unique characters, and that most species are either highly variable, as apples and pears are, or are a collection of complex hybrids of different species, like plums. Most temperate fruits do not propagate easily by rooting cuttings, and the grafting and budding techniques, which may be well over a thousand years old, have developed as a means of routine propagation.

Not all fruit cultivars (the term used to describe varieties selected for cultivation) have been propagated by vegetative methods. Some, such as green gages, and some apples, produce very similar seedlings to their parents, and this has been used to generate whole populations of greengages, for example, which are similar, but not genetically identical clones.

Another source of variability is the ability for a tree to form a branch or small section that has mutated slightly resulting in slightly different fruit characteristics such as colour or taste. Gardeners called clones propagated from these 'sports'.

Until the sixteenth century there were numerous cultivars, especially local forms, but there was no recognizable naming process, and simple broad category names such as for apples - pippin, pearmain, codlin and costard with simple descriptive adjectives like large-leaved, sour or red, didn't separate varieties well, or permit precise and unique written descriptions. Exactly where the first 'modern' names came from is not known, but has been assumed to be a process of applying a unique and memorable name to a clone, and it is widely believed that fruit were some of the first plants to be given defining variety names, probably in seventeenth century Europe. By the time the third Thomas Rivers (1798-1877) was collecting pears and plums in France and Belgium variety names were well established throughout Western Europe.

Gerard (1597) stated he knew of sixty types of plum, Parkinson in 1629 described sixty-one, Forsyth in 1818, fifty-seven, and Lindley in 1831, sixty. Then Hogg, in 1884, listed one hundred and sixty-five. Muriel Smith listed two hundred and forty-five in the in British National Fruit Collection in 1978, a considerable reduction from the much larger number of named varieties actually sent to, or procured by, the NFC because she established that many were being grown under synonyms, but also the NFC included many accessions that had been sent to England for the first time. One of the fastest increases in plum varieties in England was between Lindley's list and Hogg's, and a similar increase is recorded over the same period for apples, pears, cherries and peaches.

The first variety names were simple fruit type names, like gage, prune, damson or verdochio. Then adjectives were applied like early, late, summer, winter, red, blue, golden, russet, then origination place names were added, like Tours, Yorkshire, Blenheim and Norfolk, later grower's, distributor's or employer's names, Cox, Coe, and Lady Sudeley, and only much later did breeders, selectors and nurserymen, the first probably Thomas or Thomas Frances Rivers, invent less descriptive, more evocative names, such as their water bird series of plums, *Swan, Bittern, Heron, Stint, Curlew* and *Mallard.* Cultivar names, originated as the basis for describing a clone, became in the nineteenth century marketing tools, and by the twentieth had become a mass of competing commercial and local names. By 1972 the plum, *Early Rivers*, was known to be sold under at least forty different names, and *Green Gage* had been shown to be identical to over one hundred samples sent in for propagation under different names to the National Fruit Trials. Today there are strict international nomenclature rules for cultivars, and as long as a name follows those rules, which the Rivers family didn't know then, and certainly didn't observe!, almost anything goes.

Fruit and the third Thomas Rivers

In the late eighteenth and nineteenth century Rivers Nursery, like Scott's, and later Laxton's and Seabrook's in the late nineteenth and early twentieth centuries, were suppliers of ornamental plants and fruit trees, to orchards, country houses, small holders and amateur gardeners selling the customers what they wanted, but also, from at least the 1820s, under the third Thomas' direction, were active in searching for new varieties to extend their range and sales, influencing their customers' choice.

Thomas Rivers was not the first to seek 'new' fruit varieties. Before him the Tradescants in the seventeenth, Coe and Knight in the eighteenth century, the Veitch family of London and Exeter in the nineteenth and several nurserymen in the fertile Thames valley market gardens to the west of London, around Brentford, were known for new fruit introductions, but from 1835 Rivers Nursery excelled. Thomas Rivers inherited the management of a family specialist rose nursery that sold fruit trees as a secondary line in 1832, but as his writings recall, was far more interested in the fruit and he followed a well worn path to find and introduce new varieties. He travelled widely in France and Belgium, and brought back to England plums, pears, figs, peaches, and grapes to extend the range the nursery sold, writing about his ideas and experiments and about how to grow fruit for gardens, and for profit.

He wrote well, in a style that we would consider far more 'modern' than that of his contemporaries, and much easier to read today than, for example, his rather verbose friend Dr Lindley of the Royal Horticultural Society. *The Miniature Fruit*

Garden, 1843, ran into twenty book editions published by Longmans, sixteen one thousand copy editions before his death in 1877. It was also a success in the USA, from 1866, with a separate publisher. In it he describes his own interest in fruit growing by describing his discovery of 'miniature trees' and their early and prolific fruiting, and as a boy scrumping in nurseries 'the hospital quarter'! He initially discovered that trees that were routinely moved and replanted in the nursery rows fruited early and well, and that this was due to the inevitable root pruning that occurred. The varieties he remembered from that time, he says about 1810, were the apples *Ribston Pippin* and *Golden Pippin.* Subsequently he designed methods to repeat this root pruning intentionally by annual replanting, a highly labour intensive technique no longer used today, later adding the use of dwarfing rootstocks, and growing in pots, for the same purpose. He, and even more his son Thomas Francis, did much to promote the use of dwarfing rootstocks for apples and pears.

His writing was certainly good salesmanship, he wrote about varieties that the nursery sold and about the rootstocks that nursery used. He wrote for everyone he thought would buy the plants, from other nurserymen to fruit farmers, large country gardens and small market gardeners. He extolled the use of dwarf rootstocks for apples, which was by no means new in England in the 1850s, the dwarf paradise stock having been introduced to England probably in the late seventeenth century, and the use of quince for pear rootstock. He proposed planting densely, as close planted espaliers and cordons, and on walls, and (following the repeal of the Window Tax) in pots in glass houses. This he described in *The Orchard House.* All these recommendations were also no doubt in recognition that a nursery could sell a customer more dwarf trees than large ones.

There were, at that time, three routes to a new fruit variety introduction. Go and find one from another country, plant it in the nursery and see if grows and crops well in the English climate. Alternatively, select a new variety by growing seed from open pollinated fruit trees, and seed from selectively cross-pollinated fruit. Lastly, selection could be made from 'discovering' desirable fruit that was growing 'in the wild', or as self sown seedlings in gardens. The first process needs travel and contacts, the second dedication and many years of effort at a time when genetics and inheritance were unknown sciences, the third depended on serendipity, but had been by far and away the most effective method for centuries. The apple, *Ribston Pippin*, the plums, *Yellow Egg,* and *Diamond* and probably *Cambridge Gage,* some of the most widely grown fruit varieties in the nineteenth century, had been 'discovered' as individual trees growing in the wild.

It can take many years to select new tree fruit varieties and now it is almost impossible to know who originated these, but within horticultural circles it is widely felt that the influence of Thomas continued throughout all the later Rivers varieties – to the point that it seems quite likely that all or almost all of them, or at least selection programmes that resulted in them, were either in existence before his death and that he was their originator. The pear Conference, exhibited at the pear *conference* in 1885, is an example.

The Rivers Nursery Orchard in 2009

It seems likely that the planting here commenced with a ploughed field, less likely grassland, or grassland that was cleared of weeds in a 2-4m wide strip into which lines of trees were planted. A grass sward throughout may have been intended in time, but only when the trees became big enough to compete with grass. Today it is grassland throughout. Most of the original trees have survived well but a few, in particular some pears and apples are noticeably restricted, which may be due to less vigorous rootstocks than others.

By the time the Rivers orchard was first planted, the influence of the earlier Rivers introductions on fruit production had declined, with the exception of the pear Conference and the plum Early Rivers. The nursery was propagating and selling what their customers wanted, or what they thought they wanted, so the varieties propagated reflect these marketing decisions.

The orchard appears to have been planted as a collection of 'mother trees', a term used at that time to describe trees cultivated to provide the 'scion' wood for propagating trees by grafting or budding. The numbers of trees of each variety in the orchard probably represented the relative importance of a variety's sales and the amount of scion wood that was estimated would be needed each year into the future.

From 1940s, when the earliest tree in the Rivers orchard may have been planted, to the late 1960s when, maybe, the last, the English fruit tree market was a very different place to that of Thomas, or Thomas Frances, Rivers, and was at the start of yet another change. In the 1950s the last standard and large half-standard trees were being planted, mostly as small farm orchards, and the trend to dense planting of dwarf bush trees was underway, culminating today in the close planting of thousands of dwarf trees to the acre. By 1970 all commercial apples and pears, especially in the east of England, were on dwarf stocks and the market was concentrating on fewer varieties. It seems likely that this new site was a rationalization of the nursery's old mother trees, previously on another orchard site, and also scattered round a large rambling nursery.

It is possible that the trees may have been planted right up to the period when the nursery no longer required scion wood from propagation, perhaps representing the need to retain a source of a variety wood because an old tree elsewhere in the nursery was in decline, or because a new variety was added to the catalogue.

Towards the end of the Rivers Nursery company's existence in the early 1980's we know that no use was made of the nursery's scion wood; fruit trees for sale were bought in as young trees from other nurseries.

It is not easy now to know what rootstocks were used. Almost certainly the apples would have been on one of the semi-vigorous Malling series of rootstocks, some may be on vigorous stocks. The pears, planted earlier, are almost certainly all on a quince rootstock, *Cydonia oblonga*, probably *Quince A*. Some are noticeably stunted by the grass around them. The plums and cherries are the largest - the plums on *St Julien A,* a selection of a very ancient small sweet green gage, once very widely grown throughout Europe, the cherries on seedling wild cherry, *Prunus avium.*

However, the absence of a particular variety does not mean that when the orchard was planted that variety was no longer propagated or sold, because throughout the nursery site there may have been many other trees scattered around in the manner of old nurseries the world over and there were other orchard sites, now lost. Nevertheless the list of varieties does represent a snapshot of what someone in the company considered needed to be available, even if the list is incomplete. It was most certainly a measure of some confidence in the future to allocate so much land to 'mother trees'. The number of trees of each variety can be taken as representing the amount of scion wood the management considered they would need for production in the future.

Apples

Rivers were not prolific apple breeders and indeed may not have bred a single apple variety. Thomas did not describe or list any apple bred by Rivers to the market in his time. Nevertheless his success in introducing and selling *Cox's Orange Pippin,* a seedling grown by Richard Cox in Buckinghamshire, was phenomenal, and later during the enthusiasms of the 1880s fruit exhibitions Rivers Nursery exhibited many apple as well as pear varieties, but few were actually marketed. Several carried the Rivers name as if they could have been their own seedlings, *Thomas Rivers, Rivers Early Peach, Rivers St Martin's* and *Rivers Nonsuch,* principally a rootstock variety propagated by suckers and clearly related to the old variety *Nonsuch.* Others, such as *Reinette D'Ore* and *Calville Vineaux* were clearly introductions from France.

The largest proportion of trees in the orchard today are apples, mostly of relatively modern varieties, and as will be seen from the notes to the list, almost entirely of varieties that came onto the market *after* the third Thomas Rivers' time. Also the number of trees per variety is high suggesting that apples made up the majority of the sales at the time they were planted, confirmed by a newspaper article from 1949 that recorded thousand of apple trees propagated and despatched to Canada, far more than pears, cherries and plums. The apple identifiers from the East of England Apples and Orchards Project that visited in 2005 were however heartened to discover trees of the culinary apple *Thomas Rivers,* one of relatively few apples introduced by Rivers over their two hundred and sixty years of existence. By the 1970s this variety was probably very rarely sold, so planting two trees each of *New Harthornden* and *Thomas Rivers* has to be some sort of recognition of the nursery's past. These varieties have unknown origins and may be, like so many other apples discovered by Rivers and shown in exhibitions, ultimately unsuccessful. The twenty-eight trees of Cox's Orange Pippin, by far the most important Rivers marketing introduction, fifteen Bramley Seedling and six Crimson Bramley perhaps put their market into perspective. The importance of the apple collection is that it represents a snapshot of the most common varieties propagated at the time of planting, with the proviso that it would have been supplemented by scion wood from the trees growing elsewhere within the nursery.

Plums and gages

Thomas, and perhaps also his son, Thomas Francis, had a considerable interest in plums, especially in dessert plums. Many plum varieties grown in England at that time were principally used for cooking, for example *Yellow Egg, Diamond* and *Imperatrice,* and only a few green gage varieties, the round green fleshed plums developed in England from the seventeenth century introductions from Italy of the variety Verdochio, perhaps identical to the *Reine Claude* in France, were eaten raw.

Several of his plum imports were not very successful, and Thomas selected seedlings from these varieties which produced better crops in the English climate, and introduced them with his own names to the market.

A list of plums recommended by Thomas in his books shows many new varieties not recorded in England before, for example by Lindley a few years earlier. Of his recommended list of twenty-eight plums in 1870, eleven are his own introductions - five of which are his own breeding or selection, the rest introductions and re-namings, and only three appear to have been listed by Lindley in 1831.

Two lines of selection in particular were successful, and well documented. One variety Thomas imported was *Precoce de Tour.* From its seedling he selected and later marketed *Rivers Early Prolific* and *Early Favourite,* two varieties that have since then confused by name changes and visual similarities, and even taste!

Another introduction from France was *Reine Claude Diaphane,* a yellowish green gage with translucent flesh, which he sold in England under a new name *Transparent Gage.* Thomas wasn't the first to change fruit variety name - it was a widely practiced marketing technique. However, it is a poor cropper in England and from it Thomas selected three of its seedlings that were better, *Early Transparent, Late Transparent* and *Golden Transparent,* although the last two were not introduced to the market until after his death.

The true Green Gages, introduced one hundred and fifty years before or even earlier, had always been a very variable crop in an English summer. Thomas's third, but less well publicized introduction and selection programme, and with less long lasting popularity, resulted in a number of new varieties developed from green gages, more accurately the French *Reine Claude* varieties brought in from the continent. Some suffered the name change routine, such as *Belgian Purple,* some retained their French names, for example *Reine Claude de Bavay,* or were direct translations, such

193

as *Oullins Golden Gage.* Other introductions are less easily attributable. *Late Orange* and other gages could have been seedlings grown in the nursery, or introductions from the continent.

From the early introductions we can see that Thomas was particularly interested in dessert plums, those that could, in the speech of gardeners, 'be eaten out of hand', rather than cooked, and also in bringing the plum season forward by selecting early fruit. This probably reflected a new market for nurserymen in the nineteenth century; there was a rising number of relatively affluent gardeners choosing to grow their own, or at least instruct their gardeners to grow them. Following from this, the range of fruit being grown by market gardeners for sale throughout the seasons for local markets was being extended to include dessert pears and plums, and from Thomas's writing it is clear that he was at all times planning that his introductions fitted the market needs. He writes about the need for a wide range of fruits to extend the seasons, early plums and late pears being crucial, and also writes, perhaps for the first time about part-time, as he calls them amateur, market gardeners and cottagers growing crops in their garden for sale in markets.

Eventually the third Thomas, and later Thomas Francis, extended their range of new introductions to entirely new culinary plums, such as *Rivers Early Damson, The Czar* and *Monarch* that were to become almost universally available varieties by the early twentieth century, and it seems likely that many of Thomas's selections were successfully introduced after his death. In many cases their origins and breeding history were largely forgotten, and Thomas was no longer alive to write about them.

Other plums introduced later just before and after Thomas' death in 1877, were named after water birds and were certainly crosses made in the nursery, and may have been a result of his breeding experiments.

As the long tail of Thomas's introductions and selections dwindled, other breeders and nurseries became more important in the nursery market, in particular Laxton and Seabrook late in the century and in the first twenty years of the next. The market had changed, amateurs were still important, but commercial market gardens and fruit farms were becoming by far the largest customers. The railways had arrived in the fens and the large commercial orchards there were interested in commercial crops, and in many cases what might be described as industrial fruit, for canning and home bottling. This last market effectively continued into the 1950s, when the vast acreages of culinary plums, currants and gooseberries rapidly declined in importance. Until then grocers sold fruit varieties specifically for home bottling, in season. This was the peak for the plums *Pershore, Burbank, Marjorie*, and of course *Victoria*. Some of the old plum varieties survived well, especially if they were free stone such as *Yellow Egg* and *Early Rivers* (most old varieties were cling stone) which reduced the labour of de-stoning, and permitted mechanical de-stoning. This resulted in Laxton's extensive range of culinary free-stone plums such as *Laxton's Cropper.*

Rivers excelled with plums. However after WWll English plum tree sales diminished and by the 1970s were being eclipsed for cool climates by early new Swedish varieties like *Opal* and *Herman.*

Nevertheless, plums in the orchard make up the second largest number of trees, over eighty, suggesting that whoever selected the varieties for propagation respected the Rivers history. Sadly the identification of plums is not easy, and as the season runs from July to October requires dedicated identifiers to visit frequently. One concentrated effort was made in August 2005 resulting in a number of identifications but many trees were not cropping and many were not in season – so that many remain unidentified. Several of Thomas Rivers' varieties were found; the many different gage varieties, some still to be identified, indicate that this is the most important gage collection in this country. The identifiers, Michael Gardner and Paul Read, both had the distinct feeling that several trees were very unusual, to the point that some they did not appear to fit any known varieties. One was sufficiently different that it was suggested that it could be a new seedling selected for trial - one of the current volunteers decided to name it temporarily *Firecrest*.

Pears

Thomas Rivers' first real love and dedication was directed at pears, for he wrote more words on pears than on any other fruit. The *beurré* pears, with succulent sweet flesh that is at its best for only a few days, if that, grow better in warmer climates than England. In the late eighteenth century most English pear trees produced either crisp and crunchy fruit, typified by the old variety *Jargonelle,* and called *crevers* in French, or were hard long keeping winter pears, called wardens or warden pears dating from the fourteenth century or earlier, which were cooked slowly with meat stews, or wine.

The *beurré* pears, relatively new to English gardens and markets, became Thomas Rivers' initial interest, and as others had done before him, he travelled to France and Belgium where nurserymen, and wealthy men of leisure, had selected varieties. *In The Miniature Fruit Garden*, or *the Culture of Pyramidal and Bush Fruit Trees,* first published in the 1840s, he recommended as many as seventy different pear varieties, many of which he introduced into the British market from France and Belgium.

George Lindley's book *A Guide to the Orchard and Kitchen Garden,* 1831, which preceded Rivers' books from Longmans, and edited by John Lindley, then assistant secretary to the Horticultural Society of London, later the Royal Horticultural Society, lists many French varieties of pear, including some in Thomas Rivers' lists, but the Rivers catalogue and those he listed in his books was far more extensive; it seems that he was responsible for many introductions. Exactly which pear varieties Thomas Introduced to the English garden and which were already in the country and in other nurseries is not always clear; he did not ever claim to have been the breeder of any pear, but he did state sometimes that a variety was 'new'. In 1870 he recommended twenty varieties, suggesting that at least ten all be grown and of these only two are not either French or Belgian, and only one was actually of English origin - Williams Bon Chretien, and introduced to Britain within the last thirty years. At least ten were introduced by him.

Although Thomas only claims in his writing to have bred or selected one pear for the English market, *Summer Beurré,* his son, Thomas Frances Rivers, did more, notably *Conference* in 1885, and it seems very likely that the breeding and selecting programme that was the origin of all Rivers pears, then rather more serendipitous than scientific, was probably started by his father.

Thomas also introduced several techniques from France that today we take for granted, grafting pears onto quince *(Cydonia oblonga)* rootstocks to create a small faster cropping bush tree. Until about 1830s pears in England were almost always grafted onto pear seedlings called 'wild pear', or onto hawthorn. Many *beurré* pears will not graft well, or securely, onto quince rootstocks, and Thomas described 'bridge grafting', which he implied he invented, whereby a short section of a pear variety that does graft securely to quince is used between the quince rootstock and the required pear variety. Today *Doyenne du Comice* is widely used as the bridge; Thomas recommended several other stocks.

The pears, about forty trees, have not been positively identified, partly due to the difficulty of bringing together a suitably experienced identification team and also because many trees have been shy of cropping, probably as result of their dwarf rootstock and competition with the grassland, so this has still to be done.

Cherries

Thomas Rivers introduced several cherry varieties, one or more of which he may have bred at Sawbridgeworth. Cherry *Early Rivers* is yet another source of name confusion. In all there was plum, a cherry, a nectarine, and a peach all called *Early Rivers,* an apple called *Early Peach*, and both an apple and a peach were named Thomas Rivers! Other cherries were almost certainly selected from elsewhere and promoted, probably, but not certainly, from within England, such as the cherry *Archduke*, not to be confused with the Rivers plum *Archduke!*, and *Turkish Black*.

The cherries in the orchard are still to be identified. I think it is unlikely that this will be done with any degree of certainty unless we have the assistance of DNA analysis. Few fruit identifiers in the Britain have any experience of cherries, and there are no accepted expert or reliable descriptions as there are with apples. The descriptions of pre-1950s cherry varieties are so imprecise that the National Fruit Collection at Brogdale, Kent, which had some two hundred and seventy varieties growing as individual trees, now considers that many of the British varieties are physically, and in taste, identical, but with different names, and that others differ so minutely that they could be the same.

The 'young trees' and the gaps

After the clearance of brambles and scrub after 1990, there were the inevitable dead trees, a considerable number of spaces, trees sites with no trees planted, and bearing in mind the obvious varying ages of the trees, it seems likely that these gaps were original, spaces left for trees still to be planted.

Since 1995 when the volunteer group started to manage the orchard quite a number of these gaps have been filled by fresh plantings of apple trees mostly, and a few others. It is known what varieties many are; others are unknown. Unfortunately most if not all appear to be on rootstocks more appropriate to gardens. Some young apple trees appear to be on very dwarfing stocks and are likely to struggle in the meadow grass ground cover – some are on the semi-dwarf MM106 which does not do well in grass and will not make trees equal the original ones unless a bare soil policy is operated for several years.

The young pears are probably on Quince A and may produce similar trees to the originals provided that they are also managed on bare soil. A list of the known recently planted varieties is held by the Rivers Nursery Site and Orchard Group.

The future

The orchard's future is not by any means certain, and this has been the driving force behind the preparation of this report, which should be considered as an initial statement to allow the proper scheduling of further work.

Rivers Nursery Orchard is a traditional orchard as defined by the Joint National Council for Conservation as a UK Priority Habitat. This is a new designation made in July 2007, in recognition of the enormous losses of the habitat in the UK as well as though out Europe in the last few decades, and the fact that many traditional orchards have been lost to development due to their frequent location close to towns and villages.

Rivers Nursery Orchard, by its size and clonal crop diversity alone, has national significance, even though many trees are still unidentified and tree surveying may continue for many years, and the wildlife diversity has yet to be properly surveyed and reported. Three areas of planning seem to me to be needed:

1   **Continued identification of the trees.**
    Plums and gages are partially identified and more effort across the wide fruit season is needed. Identification of the pears has just begun.
2   **A long term project to survey the wild biodiversity.**
    This should include a botanical survey of the ground flora, survey of the tree epiphytes, wood invertebrates, borers and saprophytes, and moth and butterfly surveys need to be extended and formalized. It is quite clear that there are important species and microhabitats present which need to be surveyed and recorded.

3   **A site management plan for the crop trees.**
    This needs to look at several key aspects of the orchard's
    future: a ground vegetation management schedule,
    boundary management, a tree management policy
    (specifically pruning), a tree planting policy - over seventy
    new trees have been planted since the nursery company
    ceased with little or no selection policy which risks blurring
    the historic importance of the site. Many of these trees are
    on inappropriate rootstocks and may never prosper, some
    would never have been appropriate to the original Rivers
    purpose.

4   **The future as a community space.**
    The orchard is beautiful and practical, and would be a
    ready-made and historically significant green space in a
    rapidly developing community. The site is about four acres
    and could contain a significant visitor population without
    problems if access was sensibly managed.

> **[Paul Read has prepared three tables to accompany this article:**
> **Table 1: A Short List of Fruit Varieties of known Rivers Origination**
> **Table 2: A List of the Fruit Varieties in the Restored Orchard planted by**
> **Rivers Nursery about 1949**
> **Table 3: A List of Young Trees planted since 1990**
> **These are available from the Rivers Nursery Orchard website:**
> **www.riversnurseryorchard.org.uk]**

Paul Read obtained his initial degree in natural sciences specializing in Botany in 1960, moved into chemistry and chemical engineering in the cinema industry, and has spent nearly 50 years in research, teaching and consultancy in a variety of fields. Today he is a consultant and peripatetic lecturer in diverse subjects including digital cinema, film and digital archiving, traditional orchard management, and farmland conservation. Clients include universities, European Union research projects, national media archives, farm conservation organisations, Natural England, county and district councils. He owns, with his wife (who does most of the work!) a small farm in Higher Level Stewardship, is a member of the Suffolk Biodiversity Partnership, and manages the Suffolk Traditional Orchard Survey. He lives at Home Farm, Great Green, Thrandeston, Suffolk. ReadHF@aol.com

Bibliography: The Rescued Orchard and the Rivers Heritage

Bunyard, Edward A., *A Handbook of Hardy fruits Apples and Pears* (London, 1920)

Bunyard, Edward A., *A Handbook of Hardy fruits Stone and Bush fruits Nuts etc.* (London, 1925)

Forsyth, William, *A Treatise on the Cultivation and Management of Fruit Trees* (London, 1818)

Gerard, John, *Catalogue of plantes,* 1596, and *The Herball, 1597* (London)

Grubb, Norman, *Cherries* (London, 1949)

Hogg, Robert, *The Fruit Manual: a guide to the fruits and fruit trees of Great Britain,* 5th Ed (London, 1884)

Lindley, George, Ed. and John Lindley, *A Guide to the Orchard and Kitchen Garden* (London, 1831)

Morgan, Joan & Alison Richards, *The New Book of Apples* (London, 2002)

Parkinson, John, *Paradisi in Sole* (London, 1629)

Rivers, Thomas, *The Miniature Fruit Garden, or the Culture of Pyramidal and Bush Fruit Trees* (London) (Many editions:1st 1843, 16th 1870, 18th 1877, subsequent editions appear identical to 18th.)

Rivers, Thomas, *The Orchard-house, or the cultivation of fruit trees in post under glass* (London, 1st Ed 1858).

Roach, F.A., *Cultivated fruits of Britain, their origin and history* (Oxford, 1885)

Scott, J., *The Orchardists,* (London, 1868)

Smith, Muriel W.G., *Catalogue of the Plums at the National Fruit Trials* MAFF (Faversham, Kent,1978)

Smith, Muriel W.G., *National Apple register of the United Kingdom* (London, 1971)

Websites

UK Biodiversity Action Plan Priority Habitat Descriptions, Traditional Orchards, *www.ukbap.org.uk/library/UKBAPPriorityHabitatDescriptionsfinalAllhabitats2008102 2.pdf*

National Fruit Collection *www.nationalfruitcollection.org.uk*. This new, 2009, website currently only has apple illustrations, but states that other fruit will follow later. The previous NFC website (downloaded by a number of private individuals in anticipation of its loss) had many other fruit including a large number of pear and plum varieties.

East of England Apples and Orchards Project *www.applesandorchards.org.uk*

General Bibliography

Anon., 'First Extraordinary Meeting', *The Cottage Gardener* (November 14, 1855)

Anon., *Journal of Horticulture and Cottage Gardener* (August 24, 1899)

Anon., 'Nursery Notes, Messrs. Thomas Rivers and Son Ltd.' *The Gardeners' Chronicle* (July 13, 1950)

Anon., 'Obituary Frank Rivers', *The Gardeners' Chronicle* (August 26, 1899)

Anon., 'Obituary, Thomas Alfred Hewitt Rivers', *The Gardeners' Chronicle* (1915)

Anon., 'The Late Mr. Rivers', *Journal of Horticulture and Cottage Gardener* (October 25, 1877)

Anon., *The Parish Church of Great St. Mary, Sawbridgeworth* (Church Guide, 2009)

Anon., 'Thomas Rivers', *The Gardeners' Chronicle* (Oct 27, 1877)

Anon., 'William Camp', *Gardeners' Chronicle* (March 20, 1926)

Anon., 'Workers among the Flowers and Fruit - T. Alfred H. Rivers', *The Garden* (December 13, 1902)

Bailey, R.H., *The Principles of Fruit-Growing* (New York, 1897)

Brace, Josh, *The Culture of Fruit Trees in Pots* (1904)

Department of the Environment, *List of Buildings of Special Architectural or Historic Interest, Sawbridgeworth*

Drake, John, Wood & Ingram, A Huntingdonshire Nursery 1742 - 1950 (Huntingdon, 2008)

Estate map for sale of Pishobury Estate, 1843 (from John Sapsford)

Fish, D.T., 'Garden Memoranda: Rivers' Nurseries, Sawbridgeworth', *The Gardeners' Chronicle and Agricultural Gazette* (1866)

Harvey, John, Early *Nurserymen* (London, 1974)

Hogg, Robert, *The Fruit Manual: A Guide to the Fruits and Fruit trees of Great Britain, 5th Edition* (London, 1884)

Read, Terence, Discussion (July, 2009)

Le Rougetel, Hazel, 'The first Rose Grower in England', *Country Life* (June 25, 1981)

Mitchell, Alan, *A Field Guide to the Trees of Britain and Northern Europe* (London, 1974)

Morgan, Joan and Alison Richards, *The Book of Apples* (London, 1993)

Munby, Lionel, *The Hertfordshire Landscape,* in *The Making of the English Landscape* Series, (London, 1977)

Munby, Lionel (ed.) *The Story of Sawbridgeworth, Book 1 From Prehistory to the Present* (Sawbridgeworth W.E.A., 1966)

Munby, Lionel (ed.) *The Story of Sawbridgeworth, Book 2 The Churches and the People,* (Sawbridgeworth W.E.A.,1966)

Pigot and Company, *National Trades Directory* (1839)

Rivers, Henry R., *Newspaper Cuttings Book 1878 - 1901.* Hertfordshire Archives and Local Studies (HALS), Acc 3607

Rivers, Thomas, 'Proposal for a Pomological Society', *The Florist, Fruitist, and Garden Miscellany* (April,1854)

Rivers, Thomas, 'Seedling Fruits', *The Gardeners' Chronicle* (1871)

Rivers, Thomas, *The Miniature Fruit Garden or The Culture of Pyramidal and Bush Fruit Trees*, eighteenth edition (London, 1877)

Rivers, Thomas, *The Orchard-House or the Cultivation of Fruit-trees under Glass*, fourteenth edition (London, 1870)

Rivers, Thomas, *The Rose Amateur's Guide*, second edition (London, 1840)

Rivers, T.F., Letter to T. Dyer, (Jan. 14, 1887, Kew Archives)

Rivers, Thomas H. *1725 - 1975: 250 Years of Thomas Rivers and Son Ltd. of Sawbridgeworth* (1975)

Seddon, V. and S. Bryant, *Sawbridgeworth: Extensive Urban Survey Project Assessment Report*, part of Archaeological Surveys by English Heritage, 1999 in Hertfordshire Archives and Local Studies (HALS).

Thick, Malcolm, *The Supply of Seeds, Plants and Trees to the Kitchen Garden and Orchard, 1600-1800,* (London, 1998)

Williamson, T., *The Origins of Hertfordshire* (Manchester, 2000),

Rivers Nursery Orchard Archives in Church House Sawbridgeworth
including *Oral History Interviews:*
Armes, Tup, Recorded Interview, 18 March 2009.

Brace, Edith, Interview, 28 February, 2007

Clark, Susan, Recorded Interview, 1 April, 2009

Elsdon, Nina, Interview, 23 January 2009

Martin, Kath Walsh, Interview 13 April, 2009.

Maskell, Vera, Recorded Interview, 18 April 2009

Powell, Joan, Recorded Interview, 26 February 2009

Richards, Diana, Recorded Interview, 10 February, 2009

Rivers, Nigel, Recorded Interview, 5 April, 2009

Rivers, Margaret, Recorded Interview, 30 March, 2009

Rivers, Peter, Recorded Interview, 5 April, 2009

Sapsford, John, Recorded Interview, 27 April 2009

Slingsby, Tony, Recorded Interview, 25 February, 2009

Smith, Robert, Research, 2009

Stubbings,Walter, Recorded Interview, 4 February 2009

Todhunter, Denis, Interview, 3 September 2008

Tybjerg, Eileen, Interview, 18 May 2007

Willison, Eric, Recorded Interview, 16 April 2009

Websites

East of England Apples and Orchards Project *www.applesandorchards.org.uk*
Darwin Correspondence Project *www.darwinproject.ac.uk*
Reads Nursery, Norfolk *www.readsnursery.co.uk*
Rivers Nursery Site and Orchard Group *www.riversnurseryorchard.org.uk*

Index

Wassailing in the 21st Century
(Rivers Nursery Orchard, Sawbridgeworth)

We never thought we'd find ourselves doing this
so why, just past the solstice
in the time of short days, do we stand in the early
evening, singing to pipe and drum beneath a canopy
of light on the underside of branches,
the air ragged with our breath which rises
through the grey warp and weft of apple trees?

It's cold; there's a hint of ice in every lungful
for this is the sharpest winter for several
years, and we have come, like so many before us,
to coax back the fugitive sun, to rouse
trees from sleep. Voices waft
with the bonfire sparks, sending songs aloft
while, overhead, small constellations turn, then drift

eastwards: how must we look from a Boeing
on approach to Stansted? We are temporary Pagans
only - unbelievers, maybe - but a flight
of wishes that these ancient rituals bring fruit
for much longer than just the coming year is loosed
with our weird music into gathering mist:
trying to touch the future, we fumble for the past.

John Godfrey